Stories from
Québec

Stories from
Québec

Selected & Introduced by

Philip Stratford

 Van Nostrand Reinhold Ltd.
Toronto/New York/Cincinnati/London/Melbourne

ISBN Cloth 0 442 27910 8
      Paper 0 442 29910 9

Library of Congress Catalogue Number 72-11215

Printed and bound in Canada by The Alger Press Ltd.

Composition by Moore Type Foundry Ltd.

Design by Pat Dacey

Cover and jacket photo by G. J. Harris.

SPECIAL ACKNOWLEDGEMENT

The editor and publisher wish to express their special thanks to the Canada Council
for providing a grant to assist in obtaining translations of the stories contained in
this book.

ACKNOWLEDGEMENTS

Grateful acknowledgement is made to those who have given permission for the use
of previously copyrighted material in this book. Every possible care has been taken
to correctly acknowledge copyright information. The editor and publisher would
welcome information that will enable them to rectify any errors or omissions in
succeeding printings. Please see the last page for complete list of acknowledgments.

74 75 76 77 78 79 80 10 9 8 7 6 5 4 3 2 1

Contents

For John, Catherine, Christopher,
Peter, Anne and Marguerite

Introduction

There is no exact translation for "short story" in French. Quebec writers don't write short stories but *nouvelles*, or *contes*, or *récits*. The English term is more generic, the French more precise. In this collection you will find examples of each of the French sub-species: The *recit* is a small slice of life with a strong historical or autobiographical bias. The *conte* is more playful, a symbolic tale which stems, in Quebec, from folklore and a rich oral tradition. It is sometimes an intellectual conceit or a contemporary parable, often a fantastic fable. The *nouvelle* is generally longer, more concerned with character, more complex and more subtley structured. I mention these distinctions because they may help the English reader to adjust to forms and treatments that will be unfamiliar. He can play the game of classification if he chooses or just enjoy the following selections as "Stories from Quebec."

There are several characteristics common to all of them, however, that should be pointed out as typically Québecois. One is the joyful sense of the traditional tale-teller that all the stories convey. This spirit is well illustrated in Jacques Ferron's stories, particularly in "Martine" where one story leads to another, which calls forth a third, which makes its point by a further fable. Each speaker in this narrative conversation reveals himself by telling a tale, and the sum of the stories cross-referenced and woven together makes up fabric of the whole.

With less virtuosity perhaps, but with an equal relish, writers as different as François Hertel and Roger Fournier, as Claire Martin and Jacques Renaud obey the same basic compulsion, to spin a yarn, to captivate and tantalize their audience.

Even in more realistic stories by writers like Gérard Bessette, Jean-Jules Richard or André Major, there is a stronger sense of person behind the narrative than in most English-language short fiction. The invisible narrator and the neutral style have never had much vogue in Quebec.

Another feature which may strike the English reader as unusual is the cataloguing of effects, a tradition that goes back to Rabelais. Instead of a dynamic plot developing in linear fashion and increasing in complexity towards a complex resolution, there is a tendency in the Quebec story (see for example, Carrier, Tétreau or Tremblay) to heap similar incident on similar incident until after much repetition and hyperbole the story reaches a sudden dénouement.

Another common characteristic is the speed and concentration of narration. Whereas the English or American short story tends to select an incident, a day, or a season for its scope in time, the Quebec writer (Gilles Vigneault or Madeleine Ferron for instance) often condenses a whole life into a few pages and even when the span is shorter writes a kind of shorthand fiction quite uncommon to American or British practice.

A trait that many readers will be looking for is the much touted morbidity of Quebec writing. It is true that there is a shipwreck, a suicide, a hanging and a bombing in these pages—no more than one finds in any daily newspaper. It is also only fair to say that the shipwreck is a farce, the suicide falls flat, the hanging ends in resurrection and the bombing in creation. And what is more impressive than the morbidity is the robust humour that underlies every one of the stories no matter how black.

The strong presence of a sanguine rather than a melancholy strain in these stories may reflect the editor's own make-up, so I feel bound to state the criteria that at least consciously directed my choice. I wanted to make a book that would represent a wide range of contemporary Quebec writers whose short fiction had never before been translated into English. This last condition was easy to fulfil; although novels by six of the eighteen writers had been translated, only Carrier, Ferron and Vigneault had had stories Englished, and it was easy, even for them, to find untranslated material. So all the work in this volume appears here in English for the first time.

As far as the "contemporary" aspect is concerned, all the writers included are still alive and active. Their ages, with one or two exceptions, range from the early thirties to the early fifties. Most of the collections from which the stories are taken were published in the past ten years. So by and large they represent the most vigorous writing done in Quebec since the start of the Quiet Revolution. Even the older writers among them if not young in years have remained young in spirit.

As for the broad range of subject and style I wished to include, that practically took care of itself. The gritty realism of Gérard Bessette was as different as possible from the neo-Gothic style of Marie-

Claire Blais; Claude Jasmin's rough vigorous transcription of life from the sinuous, elegance of Hubert Aquin. And the same applied to subject: one had only to avoid overemphasizing rural Quebec, or the city story, and the variety was there ready-made: teachers, soldiers, models, farmers, drunks, prisoners, Indians, priests, politicians and magicians, men and women, the old, the young and the middle-aged parade through these pages in a colorful cross-section of Quebec to-day.

Two things did govern and to some extent interfere with the total representivity of this collection. My decision to work in the new made me exclude all short stories from before 1945 and there are some excellent ones, by Ringuet, Grandbois, Laberge and Fréchette, which a thicker (or a second) volume might include. By the same token, I left out some talented established writers, Anne Hébert, Roger Lemelin and Gabrielle Roy, whose stories had already been translated for collections like Robert Weaver's *Canadian Short Stories*.

The second handicap I worked against, wanting to make this book as representative as possible of current Quebec writing, was that some of the authors I wished to include had written nothing in the short story form. Victor-Lévy Beaulieu is a notable case in point. I was lucky enough to get permission to publish an extract from an unpublished novel by Marie-Claire Blais in lieu of a short story, but I could not use that licence too often. As for omissions of other writers who may in time prove to be masters of the genre, I must accept full responsibility myself and put it down to quirks in my editorial taste.

This is the first book of its kind to present Quebec short stories in translation. Those who wish to read more, in French, can consult Adrien Thério's *Conteurs Canadiens-français* (Déom, 1970) and Gérard Bessette's *De Québec à Saint-Boniface* (Macmillan, 1968). The University of Ottawa Press has recently published an historical anthology *Contes et Nouvelles du Canada Français 1778-1859*, edited by John Hare, and promises more volumes in this series.

Finally a word about another unique feature of this book. The eighteen Quebec writers represented have been translated by seventeen English-Canadians. They are all skilled writers and it has been a rewarding experience to work with them. I want to thank them for their collaboration and hope that they will go on imaginatively and steadfastly in the common aim of making Quebec writers better known in the rest of Canada and the English-speaking world.

Philip Stratford

Jacques Ferron

Animal Husbandry
Martine, Continued

Jacques Ferron is, as much as he can be pinned down at all, the Grand Vizier of current Quebec letters. He made his début in drama (at the age of 28), writing his first play in 1949. After a decade in the theatre he turned to fiction, winning a Governor General's prize for *Contes du pays incertain* in 1962, translated as *Tales from the Uncertain Country* by Betty Bednarski (Anansi, 1972), and publishing another collection *Contes anglais* in 1964 from which these two selections are taken. Since then he has become a major force in the novel, creating sardonic myths, satirical fantasies and farcical *roman-à-clef* which typify the political mores and cultural idiosyncrasies of modern Quebec.

The typical Ferron story is speedy and spare: it wraps up a life in a couple of pages, tacks down a major event in a few paragraphs, pinpoints a conventional attitude in a phrase, captures a character in a sprig of dialogue. The stories are told with the objectivity of the ballad or folk tale and like these make liberal use of irony and fantasy. All are written with drollery, wit and great grace of style.

Larry Shouldice, the translator of these stories, is managing editor of the bilingual review *Ellipse*, teaches at l'Université de Sherbrooke and l'Université du Québec à Trois-Rivières, and is writing a doctoral dissertation on winter imagery in French- and English-Canadian poetry.

Animal Husbandry

I went
to a private
school, at the
end of the
Fontarabie
county road. The schoolmistress
was a small, down-to-earth widow with a bad
reputation, nicknamed l'Allumette. She told me about the
night life of Paris, and showed me the underside of life. I
came out of there quite depressed, followed by a pensive elephant
with a sad trunk. The people of Fontarabie, seeing me go by like this,
felt I was overdoing it. I couldn't help it and it was most embarrassing. But then, to make matters worse, the elephant got sick,
in the trunk, of course. I took him to Montreal to see a doctor. The
doctor said he was honoured, that it was a sickness one could be
proud of, and he cured me of it so quickly and completely that I found
myself, elephantless, riding a galloping unicorn back towards the
lovely county of Maskinongé. Three black dogs were with me, their
eyes red and their mouths on fire. It was more than I could possibly
have hoped for. So, when I got to Sainte Ursule, instead of going on
to Fontarabie, I spurred on towards the rectory. The dogs were tum-
bling around in the flower beds. I went in alone with my unicorn.

"A nice animal," said the priest.

"Sure, it's a nice animal, but it's leading me straight to hell."

And I showed him the wild black dogs sitting on their haunches in
the flower bed, their mouths on fire, like real hell-hounds.

"You'd better get married," said the priest.

A week later it was done. My wife spoke as soft as a Charlesbourg
mouse. She called me her big white rat. What could be more restful,
especially after the elephant and the unicorn! I was happy and con-
tent. My wife could do anything she wanted with me. One fine

morning she found a rat on the pillow, a big white rat. It was I. Now she was free as you please. At last she could open the closet in which, caught short by my proposal, she had locked up her lover a few days earlier. Out came the lover and my wife dusted him off. They were happy to see each other again. Meanwhile, I was running around the pillow.

"What's that?" asked the lover.

"It's a big white rat," replied my wife.

"A big white rat? Okay. But couldn't he run around somewhere else?"

"No," said my wife.

The lover was amazed.

"It's my husband," she added.

He wasn't surprised any more, but I kept on bothering him just the same; whenever he forgot about me, I would nibble his ears. A week later nothing was left of the love between them. He was always keeping an eye on me, and that had changed his looks. Why was he watching me like that? Innocently, I moved closer. With all his claws out he pounced! But I was expecting it, and immediately I barked. That took him completely by surprise. He couldn't get over it. It was a cat who ran away, not a lover. I chased him lazily, for fun, to stretch my limbs a bit, and then I returned and lay my muzzle on the knees of my unfaithful wife.

"Silly fool," she said, "why don't you grow up and be a man?"

That was all I was hoping for. And so it came to pass that, after various transformations, I became a good husband.

Martine, Continued

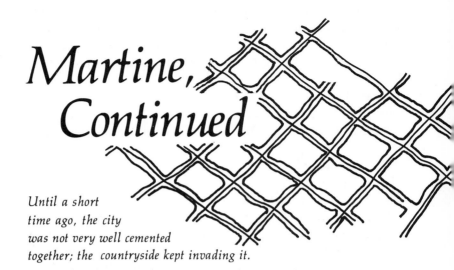

*Until a short
time ago, the city
was not very well cemented
together; the countryside kept invading it.*

MARTINE

My father used to be an exuberant man whose generous wife presented him with a child every year and never gave it a second thought. She remained rosy-cheeked and beautiful, as comely as the house, which was clean and bright under the willows. We owned several acres of land around the house, enough to feed a cow and her calf, and some pigs. I was brought up with these animals, which is why I keep healthy. The city, however, having encircled our domain, kept gnawing away at it insidiously. My father let one piece of land go, then another, and then a third, so that in the end there wasn't enough hay for the cow. She went dry, and what can you do with a cow that doesn't give milk except eat her? Which we did.

The next spring we had no calf. My father ended up selling the little island of countryside on Mount Royal Street which, without the cow and her calf, had lost its meaning. Finally, it was the pigs' turn. When the last one had been eaten, the neighbours moved closer. They glued their houses to ours. We were caught up in the whole thing. And my mother started to suffer from shortness of breath.

The countryside, which had slipped in through the cracks to the very heart of the city, with cows, pigs, chickens, vegetables and trees, retreated little by little, taking back its animals, the clean air, and the joy. The houses, welded to each other, still kept their role as dwellings, but also served now as walls. The cracks were repaired. No more escape, no more space: now the city was well cemented together.

THE WINO

I didn't used to be a wino. I was something more honourable: a vagabond. Not the kind who frightens women and is given a penny to keep away bad luck, but the kind of vagabond known throughout the province, who is welcomed with joy and even asked to stay, for he brings wisdom and dreams in his pack. As long as the mild season lasted, I would keep to the roads. At night I would stop in some house where I would spend the evening conjuring up before the eyes of my hosts a world that had no reality, but through which you could still perceive the one that had been swallowed up by the shadows. The next day, on the road again, I would feel that I hadn't come in vain and that I had left behind more order than before: a brighter day, the farms more clearly set out, faces more human. No, I wasn't a tramp. I didn't beg for anything, and what I received couldn't be compared to what I had given. I was a bum, but I was also kind of a great lord wandering the world to give it a bit more substance, to give it a little style.

THE WIDOWER

I was young when a passer-by, unknown in the village, looked behind my ears and predicted to my father that I would never be happily wed. My father remembered this when the time came for me to marry. He chose me the gentlest and humblest of girls. Never was there a more tender wife in the whole world. But she died, and I loved her. The passer-by hadn't been wrong.

THE WINO

In winter I'd come back to town and find my buddies again; then they were vagabonds, now they're winos. We would exchange wisdom and dreams, waiting for the end of the flood. For winter is a flood. Each house becomes an ark in which the memory of springtime lives on; that's how the springtime returns again. We would watch for it, and as soon as the air was quivering with an aimless desire, as soon as its shining sign appeared, we would quickly say good-bye to one another. Each would take up his pack of wisdom and dreams and discreetly leave town. The winding roads were good for roving, and walking was still possible. A horse doesn't go much faster than a man and the difference isn't worth the trouble of an extra animal. We moved along at a lively pace. Sometimes, in one season, we could visit the whole province.

Then the horses disappeared, replaced by machines. The roads 5 + *Martine Continued* became straighter and harder. It was no longer possible to walk. How can you expect a man to compete with those speed machines that tear through space on ribbons of smoking asphalt? Walking didn't get you anywhere any more; you were just as far ahead to stay put. So we stopped roving. Without our tales the country became confused again.

We don't leave the city now, and we've swapped our packs for the bottle; we've traded wisdom and dreams for poison. Wisdom and dreams don't belong in the city, but the bottle gives us a taste of the great escape.

MARTINE

When we had eaten the cow, the calf, and the pigs, my father took to drink, and misfortune struck our household. His wife became an awful thing, a withered mass of sallow flesh, who still found strength enough to wield a broom. You can guess the rest of my story. Oh my, yes, she really used to lay into me! Still, I can't forget my childhood and happiness for me is a cow chewing her cud near Mount Royal Street, or a cup of warm milk with a bit of froth on it, just enough to leave a white moustache under your nose.

The countryside used to come into the city, while the tramps with packs on their backs were leaving it. Between the country and the city there was an exchange of wisdom and health. But now this trading has stopped. The city has kept its goods and the country hers, so each has lost everything, both wisdom and health. The one doesn't come without the other. Exchanges are sometimes necessary. A fable will help you to understand.

THE WINO

Once there was a man who was a widower. He had large ears and a daughter, and this daughter was courted by a boy who was the son of another widower, and this widower had ears as large, as red, and as shameful as those of the first. Which is not surprising, since outlandish ears seem to favour widowerhood. Friendship consoled the two men in their fate, and this gentle bond not only promoted their children's friendship but also made their work more effective.

Mutual help is necessary on continents, and all the more so on a deserted island. The two widowers had landed on such an island one morning, each with a child on his back, after a shipwreck from which they were the only survivors. They had not landed together. The

Martine Continued + 6

widower with the daughter built his house in the north of the island, while the widower with the son built his in the south. Then, having met each other while out exploring and struck up a friendship, they decided to farm in the middle of the island so that they could work together. Theirs was an equal friendship; one didn't have to walk any farther to work than the other.

The children, however, were keeping house, one in the north and one in the south, and it was by chance that they came to know each other. Down on the shore the boy picked up a little compass that had been left there after his father's shipwreck, and it led him straight to the girl. Love itself couldn't have guided him better, for which we can be thankful; otherwise he might have drowned. There are attractions that lead towards life as well as towards death and love is one of these. This time, thanks to the compass and the positions of the two houses, love was well directed. While the fathers were labouring in the middle of the island, the children, in the house to the north, were practising to become lovers. A beard sprouted on the boy; a sigh stirred the girl. Their passion increased as the days went by. The girl sighed so well and so often that her bosom remained swelled from a sigh that she couldn't let out. These burgeoning breasts and the budding beard called forth other amorous weapons.

The young lovers at last were on the point of confrontation when, most inopportunely, the widowers with the big ears, catching wind of something, stopped working harmoniously in the middle of the island, took off their masks of friendship and showed each other faces of hostility. Their children's skirmishing was none of their business; why were these two old fools interfering? Widowers have strange ways and these two, because their children were falling in love, set out to kill one another. Then they thought it would be safer to go back home, one to the house in the south, and the other to the house in the north, in which the latter found the son of his new enemy. He booted him out the door with vigorous kicks to the backside. Jack and Jill were separated. It was the end of their romance; the blossom did not bear fruit. The lovers were kept confined by the widowers, each of whom cleared a garden around his own house. The middle of the island became wild and overgrown with underbrush. The lovers' hearts, likewise.

After two years of this regime, the son of the widower in the south was a vague, nervous, sickly creature, no longer a boy. The daughter of the widower in the north was a vague, nervous, sickly 7 + *Martine Continued* creature, no longer a girl. And the widowers' ears stuck out in anguish. One night they heard footsteps. The next morning, in the undergrowth in the middle of the island, they found the two children. They had come back together again to die.

The fable doesn't tell us anything more. What became of the widowers? Were they changed into donkeys? It's quite probable but the fable doesn't say. It has nothing more to say than to make us understand that among human beings certain exchanges are necessary.

Exchanges are necessary between lovers, between the mind and the body, between the city and the country. But a thousand rows of walls enclose the city, and the imprisoned lovers only meet again in death. The wedding procession gets lost in the underbrush and is replaced by a funeral procession. No one can cry out. Substitutions are made without anyone protesting them, and in an anguished silence the undertakers are always ready to take advantage of dissension. Exchanges are necessary between two shores, but the bridges have been burned. Above the common waters the willow branches are no longer intertwined from bank to bank. The arch between the two walls has fallen, and hands reach out to the sky without joining. Exchanges are necessary among men, but men group together in isolation. They would like to get along but are unable to speak to one another. They arrange to meet and then slam the door in each other's face. Everyone, in an inner prison, is his own jailer. And there are some in vaults who see their own agony through the eyes of an undertaker. A lonely man is his own prey. Solitude is the sign of our times. There are no more exchanges; there is no more society. A grotesque discordance reigns supreme, and in the thin air the wing of oblivion brushes the world.

THE WINO
I don't feel its approach anymore. For a long time now I've been hearing the whistle of its wings. Haven't you noticed it?

MARTINE
A shadowy and bloody wing it is, herding the flocks before it. Men come to me, absurd and pitiful. At least rats, when they panic, throw themselves in droves into the sea. But men keep up appearances; they stay in line, hats in hand, in spite of their anguish. And they come to me for God-knows-what deliverance, as if I could open the world to them. Their lovemaking seems to be a last escape. They press against me and tumble me, but it's all in vain. A bit of a tumble can generate a lot of emotion, but it can't alter fate.

Martine Continued + 8

SALVARSAN

If oblivion threatens the world, men, for their part, are spreading madness. We live in a strange age.

The world evolves, but the forms in which we apprehend it barely change. Apprehending the world changelessly, we think nothing. It follows that mind without nourishment breeds a creeping uneasiness.

SALVARSAN

My breath came shorter. *I'm getting old,* I thought. And my temperament changed. I felt a greater pity for my patients; their recovery brought me a quicker joy. When I received my fees, I compared myself to the girl who, having given herself willingly, found it painful to hold out her hand. Poverty, along with the humiliation of an inferior situation, is the cause of a lot of sickness and many premature deaths. Attending one of these deaths, I had the feeling that I was participating in a human sacrifice. More clearly every day I could see behind the social system a blood-thirsty idol, greedy for children, young men and young women. I called him Baal. I could have found other names for him. My sense of perspective had changed and medicine began to seem rather futile.

THE WIDOWER

My wife accidentally swallowed a germ that stayed in her chest, and it was impossible to get rid of it. And yet she took all the drugs. As the doctor said, science is not yet perfect. The day will come, however, when there will be an effective drug for every germ. Men will keep on dying, but it will be from natural causes. A natural death is the flower of old age.

SALVARSAN

Once upon a time there was a man whose son was condemned to death. I don't know why. This man, crazed by his sorrow, imagined that he would save his son by killing the hangman. And it was a second hangman who executed both the son and the father.

THE WINO

Another time there was a young prince who lived in the most beautiful castle in the world. His father was the king of the land. When he was twenty years old he fell into a sort of leth- *9 + Martine Continued* argy. He had no desires. The finest foods nauseated him. The king summoned his doctors, but their knowledge was useless. As a last resort wise men were sent for. Yet they were as foolish as the doctors, except for one of them who said to the king, "Sire, in the city there is an old lady who is dying of hunger. By saving her you will save your son." The old woman was given food, and the young prince again found the will to live. The next day, however, he fell back into his lethargy. The king summoned the wise man again. "There is," said the wise man, "a baby who is crying from thirst. His mother has no more milk, and his father is not rich enough to buy cow's milk for him." The baby was given milk to drink, and the young prince again found the will to live. But the next day he fell back into his lethargy. "There is," said the wise man, "a young girl who has been badly done by and who..." The king interrupted, shouting that there would be no end to it. "No replied the wise man, for there is no end to human misery." And the king, who loved his palace and his banquets, let his son, the young prince, die.

No one mends old clothes with new cloth, for the new patch pulls away part of the clothing and the tear becomes worse. Neither is new wine stored in old casks . . . .

MARTINE
To keep the old casks they have sacrificed the new wine. The blood of our children flows in the mud.

Madeleine Ferron

Sugar Heart
Be Fruitful and Multiply

Madeleine Ferron is Jacques Ferron's younger sister. She has published a novel, *Le Baron écarlate* (1971), and two collections of short stories, *La Fin des loups-garous* (1967) and *Coeur de sucre* (1966). The two stories included here come from the latter collection.

Her stories have the same clarity and swiftness as her brother's, but she is more sensual than he is, an observer rather than a fabulist, and displays much more direct empathy with her subject. Her poetic stories have a natural rhythm and an inner serenity that recall *The Double Hook*, which is why I asked Sheila Watson to translate them.

Sheila Watson, Professor of English at the University of Alberta, is the author of one of Canada's finest novels, *The Double Hook*, and has written some brilliant short stories of her own. This is her first translation.

Sugar Heart

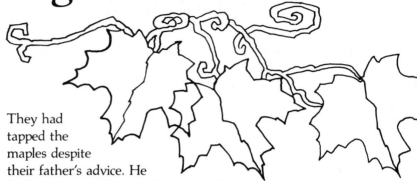

They had
tapped the
maples despite
their father's advice. He
had interpreted the timid activity of spring in
the light of his own experience and wanted them to postpone the
tapping for another week. They were nineteen and twenty years old.
The impatience and carelessness of the young often seem like
boldness. Their elders, impressed, sometimes yield to them and learn
something.

"It is too soon," their father grumbled to clear his own conscience.
"You will have to tap again."

The boys began to laugh. One worked the brace and bit and the
other drove in the spigots.

"Shall we tap the small maples?" they cried. "It's good for them to
force them a little."

"Perhaps," their father answered, "but from the big ones on the
knoll don't take more than two pails each."

"Bah, they can give four at least," the sons said.

The father objected stubbornly. One year he too had been excited.
Just above the slope, there had been an enormous maple, a beauty.
He had taken ten pails. "Ten, do you hear!" Well, he had drained the
soul from her. In the summer she had dried up.

The following night, an unexpected frost, a hard frost, urged on
the sap. The next day the sun was hot and the maples began to run.
When the father and his two sons returned to the bush after dinner,
the pails were half filled and reflected dazzling shafts of broken sunlight. The air was motionless and soft as velvet. The mounds of
snow, melted on the surface, had frozen almost at once into spark-
ling hummocks. To look one had to screw up one's eyes. In the distance the crows cawed and soon the boys, who were gathering sap,

shouted at the top of their voices. The horse, responding indifferently to contradictory orders, pulled the sledge as if habit directed its feet. When they had made the rounds the boys came back to the shack riding the runners, their snowshoes on their backs, their forelocks plastered to their foreheads. Their faces were covered with sweat. Drenching their shirts, it gave off the smell of young animals.

"Light up," they called. "The barrel's full."

On the doorstep, the father shook his head, proud and pleased that his children had been right. And then he felt filled with joy to discover, unchanged as it was each year, the pleasure of the first kindling of the flame: the first stir one gave to the boiling sap, like the first sheaf of grain harvested, gave him an almost sensual satisfaction.

And the soft white smoke rose from the chimney, light and soft as silk, at times so transparent that it was visible only as it disturbed a band of blue sky that stirred and rippled. The boys came out of the shack, listening. Distant voices, still scattered, sounded from the road that came up through the bush. They approached slowly and soon became clearer and more numerous. At the last turn of the path, the voices separated. Some even proclaimed their identity. The older boy, the twenty-year-old, before he saw the group, had recognized Alice's voice, a low voice, a little strained, which disturbed and excited him.

A dozen young people emerged from the woods. The girls suddenly began to laugh a laugh that nothing seemed to provoke and the boys to jostle one another in the snow. They arrived at the shack arms entwined or hand in hand.

"See how nice we are? We have come up to visit you," Alice said in a voice tuned to the sway of her hips. The twenty-year-old shuffled, threw back the hair from his face, and asked them to come in. They preferred to stay outside, they said, and began to perch on the uneven piles of wood—low in the centre and heaped up at the sides. Under the roof that descended above them, turned toward the sun, they settled as if in a niche.

The father, inside the shack, was preoccupied with his own generation. Memories rose in him, many of them so vivid that it seemed for a moment he had recovered them whole and almost palpable. He closed his eyes. His memory denied him coldly and the images he strove to recover slipped away, casting off only one or two details, precise, clear, always the same, which he could not connect with any *13 + Sugar Heart* event. He came out of the shack and told the boys to watch the fire, he was going down to the house. They replied in unison with excessive warmth. Attentive and silent, they watched their father withdraw. All the time the music of sap dropping into the empty pails could be heard, the muffled sound of the snow collapsing in blocks, and soon the creak of horseshoes on the snow and the metallic noise the harness fittings make when the horse holds back the load instead of hauling it. Before breaking the silence, someone whispered, "Listen." It was the gurgle of the melted stream, its voice soft and happy as the waking wood when life frees itself each spring. "It makes me thirsty," said a boy waving a bottle of whisky. "Get some syrup."

After the second round they threw their caps in the air. Their windbreakers and sweaters had become cushions, covers spread out on the cordwood. In front of the lean-to several steps away a large flat stone, still steaming at the edge, emerged from the snow. A boy wiped his mouth organ on the sleeve of his shirt. Resting his head against a log, his eyes half closed, he began to play. Another jumped down from the woodpile, leaped up and landed legs bent and arms crossed like a Russian dancer, and jigged his way over to the flat stone.

The world shrank, warm and small. It scarcely extended beyond the boundary traced by the circling bottle of whisky. On the flat stone one dancer followed another. The harmonica went from mouth to mouth while hands clapped to keep the rhythm. The music accelerated its beat. It rose. It fell headlong. Dancer and musician taunted, provoked, enflamed each other and soon reached a paroxysm where knots untie and power liberates to enter into other combinations and weave new spells.

It was then that Alice got up. While she was walking to the stone she loosened her hair. Drenched in light, it swayed softly at her back. "Give me the mouth organ," the boy of the house, the twenty-year-old, said. "I'm the one who'll make her dance." Uncertain at first, the cadence soon became flexible and controlled. The rhythm had yielded, obeyed. A theme emerged. It was precise, renewed without interruption, deep and obsessive as a message repeated endlessly by drums in the forest. Mysterious and catlike, Alice's body came alive in jerky movements and wild gestures. Then it composed itself, became attentive, bent under the stress of the music, fused more and more with the rhythm, found itself joined to the musician in quiet surrender. As she turned, she opened her arms and still dancing slipped out of her sweater, which flew away and fell limp and shapeless on the snow. She unhooked her slacks which fell, cutting the line of her hip. The skin on her shoulders, her belly, her breasts, was reddened with cold and gilded by the sun. The musician stood erect, flaming crimson like a field poppy.

The sun suddenly went down behind the forest, ending the scene. They came to again, looked at one another, startled, sober, already chattering with cold. "Brr!" said Alice putting on her sweater, filling it out again. They scurried around, picking up their caps, quickly put on their clothing, and hurried away like a flock of sparrows surprised by the wind.

Be Fruitful and Multiply

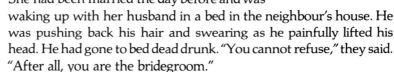

About eight o'clock they woke with a start. Amazed and confused, she shrank from the unexpectedness of her waking. She wasn't dreaming. It was true. She had been married the day before and was waking up with her husband in a bed in the neighbour's house. He was pushing back his hair and swearing as he painfully lifted his head. He had gone to bed dead drunk. "You cannot refuse," they said. "After all, you are the bridegroom."

Half way through the evening he was drunk already and a shock of brown hair had fallen forward over his face without his making any effort at all to throw it back with a shake of his head as he usually did. Shifting from leg to leg, her senses blunted with sleep, she watched, heavy-eyed, the progress of the festivity, diverted from time to time by the almost wild pleasure he was taking in his own wedding feast.

Since it was her wedding too, she resolutely stayed awake, all the while envying her cousin who slept peacefully, her head against the corner of the wall. They were the same age—thirteen-and-a-half. At that age sleep could be pardoned, she had heard them say again and again. Of course, but not on the night of one's wedding.

It was long after midnight when at last he signalled her to follow him. They went through the garden so that no one could see them or play mean tricks on them. She helped him to jump over the fence, to cross the ditch, and to climb the stairs. He fell across the bed and began to snore at once, his hands clenched like a child's. He was eighteen. She slept, curled round on an empty corner of the mattress.

They got up quickly as soon as they woke, ashamed to have stayed in bed so long. He ran to hitch up a buggy which he drove around in front of his in-laws' house. His wife's trunk was loaded on and he helped her up. He was formal, embarrassed; she, almost joyful. Then he turned the horse at a trot towards the property that had been prepared for them. He was to be the second neighbour down the road. She waved happily again and again and her mother, who was crying, kept watching, until they had rounded the corner, the blond braid that swung like a pendulum over the back of the buggy seat.

All day they worked eagerly getting settled. In the evening they went to bed early. He embraced her eagerly. Face to face with a heat that flamed and entangled her in its curious movement, she was frightened.

"What are you doing?" she asked.

He answered quietly, "You are the sheep and I am the ram."

"Oh," she said. It was simple when one had a reference point.

On the first mornings of their life together, after he had left for the fields, she ran quickly to her mother's.

"Are you managing?" her mother always asked.

"Yes," the child replied smiling.

"Your husband, is he good to you?"

"Oh yes," she said. "He says I am a pretty sheep."

Sheep . . . sheep. The mother, fascinated, watched her daughter attentively but did not dare to question her further.

"Go back to your husband now," she said. "Busy yourself about the house and get his meal ready."

Since the girl hesitated uncertainly as if she did not understand, her mother sprinkled sugar on a slice of bread spread with cream, gave it to her and pushed her gently toward the door. The child went down the road eating her bread and the mother, reassured, leaned sadly against the wall of the house watching the thick swaying braid until the girl turned the corner of the road.

Little by little the young wife spaced her visits. In autumn when the cold rain began to fall, she came only on Sundays. She had found her own rhythm. Was she too eager, too ambitious? Perhaps she was simply inattentive. Her tempo was too swift. She always hurried now. She wove more bed covers than her chest could hold, cultivated more vegetables than they could eat, raised more calves than they knew how to sell.

And the children came quickly—almost faster than nature permits. She was never seen without a child in her arms, one in her belly, and another at her heels. She raised them well, mechanically, without counting them; accepted them as the seasons are accepted; watched them leave, not with fatalism or resignation but steadfast and untroubled, face to face with the ineluctable cycle that makes the apple fall when it is ripe.

The simple mechanism she had set in motion did not falter. She was the cog wheel that had no right to oversee the whole machine. Everything went well. Only the rhythm was too fast. She outstripped the seasons. The begetting of her children pressed unreasonably on that of her grandchildren and the order was broken. Her daughters and her sons already had many children when she was still bearing others—giving her grandsons uncles who were younger than they were and for whom they could have no respect.

She had twenty-two children. It was extravagant. Fortunately, as one child was carried in the front door, beribboned and wailing, one went out the rear door alone, its knapsack on its back. Nevertheless, it was extravagant. She never realized it.

When her husband was buried and her youngest son married, she caught her breath, decided finally on slippers and a rocking chair. The mechanism could not adjust to a new rhythm. It broke down. She found herself disoriented, incapable of directing the stranger she had become, whom she did not know, who turned round and round with outstretched arms, more and more agitated.

"And if I should visit my family?" she asked her neighbour one day. She had children settled in the four corners of the province, some even exiled to the United States. She would go to take the census or, rather, she would go like a bishop to make the rounds of the diocese.

She had been seen leaving one morning, walking slowly. She had climbed into the bus, a small black cardboard suitcase in her hand. She had smiled at her neighbours but her eyes were still haggard.

She went first to the States. She was introduced to the wife of her grandson who spoke no French and to all the others whom she looked at searchingly.

"That one," she said, "is she my child or my child's child?"

The generations had become confused. She no longer knew.

She went back to Sept-Isles. One day, when she was rocking on the veranda with one of her sons, he pointed out a big dark-haired young man who was coming down the street.

"Look, mother," her son said. "He is my youngest." He was eighteen and a shock of hair fell forward over his face. She began to

cry.

"It is he," she said. "It is my husband."

The next day she was taken to the home of one of her daughters, whom she called by her sister's name. Her daughter took care of her for several days and then took her to the house of the other daughter who, after much kindness, took her to the home of one of the oldest of the grandsons. She asked no questions. She cried.

Finally, one of her boys, chaplain in a home for the aged, came to get her. She followed him obediently. When he presented her to the assembled community, she turned to him and said quietly, "Tell me, are all these your brothers?"

François Hertel

The Shipwreck

François Hertel (Rodolphe Dubé) was born (1905) before his time. An erratic revolutionary before the "quiet revolution", a separatist before separatism, he was in and out of the Church, lived in self-styled exile in Paris for twenty years, published voluminously and unevenly—essays, poems, plays, novels—and disagreed with everyone.

His story, "The Shipwreck", is black Leacock with a dash of W.C. Fields. A detailed comparison between it and "The Sinking of the Mariposa Belle" would do a great deal for national understanding. Its callous gallic charm may at first sight seem very different from Leacock's nostalgic nonsensical humour. But both writers are masters of ironic understatement and both share the same comic mistrust of human nature.

"The Shipwreck" comes from a collection of short stories called *Jérémie et Barabbas*, first published in Quebec in 1966. The other stories show Hertel's versatility, but all have the same shorthand elegance and are as fanciful and unpredictable as snow.

Philip Stratford, editor of this volume also edited recently *The Portable Graham Greene* and *André Laurendeau: Witness for Quebec*.

The Shipwreck

The sun sank. The sea
rose. Abandon ship. There were
still fifty souls on board. When the vessel
capsized everyone set out on his own particular adventure.

George grabbed a plank. They were five hundred yards from shore
and George was fond of bragging that if he had wanted to he could
have swum the Channel. Maybe so. But to swim the Channel of
one's own free will, and to be tossed willy-nilly into the sea, is not the
same thing at all.

Anyway, George kept a good grip on his plank. Thanks to it he
stayed afloat. The waves were so huge that he swallowed a mouthful
now and then, but he wouldn't have let go his plank for the world.

As for Catherine, she could hardly swim a stroke. That's why the
plucky lass made no fuss but simply set out for shore. On the beach a
deploring populace contemplated the catastrophe. It's safe to say that
the majority of the bystanders preferred to be there rather than out
at sea. That's why they didn't budge. Many could swim. Few let on.
Wasn't it better to grieve than drown? The most any of the men did
was shout out from time to time: "I'm going to dive in and save those
poor beggars!"

But at that, not a single woman raised a voice in protest. Everyone
knew that nobody was going to dive into the sea. There were
enough people out there already.

What do you expect? When there are a bunch of people bobbing
around in it like that, the sea loses its docile, childlike character altogether. It's no longer "the Sea, great Mother of us all" that poets talk
about. It's rather (if you'll pardon an easy pun), a great Mother-in-
Law, snappish and crabby.

Jean was sprawled out, for better or worse, belly down on a case of canned goods. Jean was a champion swimmer, but he really only knew how to swim the hundred metres. He was used to short distances in the swimming pool. Jean didn't like the salt water. It stung his face. Since he had never swum slowly, he wasn't sure he could make five hundred yards.

As for Brother Cornelius—who couldn't swim, wasn't much good at getting out of scrapes, and didn't cling to life all that doggedly anyway, as he counted on a much gayer time in eternity—he simply let himself founder. A miracle! He wouldn't sink. At least not yet. Just the same, he felt that things couldn't go on like this and that he was bound to sink sooner or later. He filled the time reciting one act of contrition after another. He was really contrite. But, he wasn't exactly sure in which particulars he had offended God, the poor innocent.

Catherine was doing fine. She had swum a good two hundred yards and wasn't too tired. Her long blonde hair had come undone and floated out around her in the salt water.

The Captain stood in the water up to his neck, taking his clothes off. He swore under his breath as he did so. He was disgruntled at the thought of arriving ashore in the nude. Without his uniform, would he still please the ladies he had buttered up with his fine talk and fancy manners? The ladies stood to gain something from his predicament, but what about himself? Moreover, he was a difficult fit, being somewhat portly. On this almost desert island where he was destined to land, would they be able to make him a decent uniform? The Captain undressed slowly, phlegmatically. Since it was his sixth shipwreck, and he had previously swum a distance of two miles, he was singularly calm. He wasn't thinking about helping anyone else either. *God helps them,* he thought to himself, *who help themselves.*

"Well, there she goes," he said as the ship went down.

Like all good captains, he was, naturally, the last to leave, knowing full well that there wasn't any danger.

"Help!" called the first mate, who couldn't swim and hadn't found so much as a toothbrush within reach.

Good riddance! thought the Captain, who had just begun to set out for shore with a long, unhurried stroke.

Catherine was getting near shore. A strong, tall young man made his way out to her, the water up to his chin. A rope secured him to land; there were a good ten people on the other end. He seized Catherine. She suddenly felt a wave of emotion and fainted. It was not without a glow of pride that the strapping youth deposited her on the beach and began to administer artificial respiration.

But I was forgetting George and his plank. They were still floating, both of them, but a nasty current had carried them out to sea. Though George knows how to swim (and how!) he doesn't dare take the plunge. He sees several poor souls going down around him, whom he could have helped, but he doesn't dare. He feels like a heel, but there's no other way.

But where are the lifeboats? You can hardly see them. They've all gone out to sea. You'd think they were trying as hard as they could to get away from the island. What will become of them?

The Chaplain has just caught up with Brother Cornelius. The Chaplain is an ex-scout, so he has learned swimming. He swims right past Brother Cornelius, graciously dispensing an absolution on his way. For that matter, he swims in zigzags absolving everyone, even the Israelites.

The Rabbi has just gone under. No doubt he felt a breath of absolution passing over the surface of the sea.

The Chaplain has kept his cassock on. So has Brother Cornelius.

The following have just given up the ghost: the chief cook, the bottle washers, the stokers—all those in fact whose laborious childhoods never left them the leisure to learn how to swim. Too bad.

Miss Veronica, who had fallen into the water with her umbrella, doesn't know how to swim either. For other reasons, of course. When she was a girl one didn't, in her family, show one's fanny. At any rate, she won't suffer much. She's too dried up to float very long.

All in all we've got a really great shipwreck going. There will only be a dozen or so deaths among the swimmers. As for the people in the lifeboats, they'll end up somewhere.

On the shore our heroes are busier than ever. The Chaplain is one of the first to land. With great dignity, despite his streaming cassock, he absolves everyone, indiscriminately: the islanders, the living, the dead, and Catherine who, a little pale, disengages herself from the arms of her rescuer.

Catherine is saved. Bravo!

Jean is within a hundred metres. He releases his case of canned goods which bounds up on the crest of a wave, possibly to crash down on the head of some other swimmer. He makes it to the beach in beautiful style. He must have beaten the record for the hundred metres. He steps proudly ashore, just at the very moment that the chief electrician founders.

On his involuntary trip out to sea, George has linked up with one of the lifeboats. Grumbling and cursing, they pull him in. He suggests that they try to get closer to the island. They tell him that all he had to do was go there himself in the first place.

On the boats there's a lot of rowing going on, but nobody rows in the same direction. They do a kind of circular mark-time. Nevertheless, everyone's happy. They're thinking about the others floating in the sea. It's not being egotistic, just realistic. That's all!

Brother Cornelius has just sunk. God save his soul!

A baby is floating in the sea. The new little Moses must have fallen out of one of the boats. Anyway, he's not even bawling. He sinks like a little soldier. Pity. An infant like that might have turned out to be somebody.

Now let's sum up. Where have I got to with everyone? Catherine saved, Jean triumphant, the Chaplain in harbour, the Captain in sight, George in a boat, and all the people on shore safe and sound. No? What's happened? The President of the Island Republic has just passed on. Too bad! A promising President.

In the long run not too many losses to mourn: the baby (by the way, whose baby was it?), Brother Cornelius (God save his soul!), Miss Veronica (R.I.P.), the first mate and the crew—just a small part of the crew for that matter, and after all, that's a sailor's trade. As for the President of the friendly Republic, tough luck. He should simply have stayed at home.

But here are more black dots on the waves. Who can these late-comers be? Great Heavens! Maryse Corolla. What happened to her? I thought she was in the first lifeboat. She was, indeed, but they tossed her out into the sea on an old mattress. (There are always a great many unexpected things in a ship's lifeboat.) She was talking too much, it seems, so they got rid of her. I would like to note here that I don't approve of such procedures.

In any case, in she comes on the waves as fresh as a flower, showing to the astonished populace the prettiest little behind you could imagine. I won't even try to describe it. The muscleman who has just revived Catherine plunges into the sea again, swimming this time, though still attached by a rope, naturally.

Maryse Corolla faints as soon as she gets near enough to shore. Artificial respiration, etc. . . .

The most touching scene, however (Damn! I forgot to list the Rabbi among the dead!) was the arrival of the Fishy Banker. His was a devilish tricky problem. "Die? Out of the question!" A Banker doesn't give up like that. "Live poor? Not likely!" Now it so happened that this Fishy Banker, or let's say rather this Shady Speculator, had a brief-case full of stocks and bonds and his pants pockets full of gold coins. He had bought a life-jacket from one of the engineers (another poor devil we won't see again) having paid for it in false stock certificates, and there he was floating heavy and upright in the sea, holding his briefcase over his head. Not exactly comfortable.

To be or not to be, that certainly was the question. What to do?

As the Chaplain stroked by he had blessed the Banker like everyone else. The Shady Speculator had seen Brother Cornelius go under. He had offered Jean ten per cent of the contents if he would carry his precious package at arm's length into shore. Then he resigned him-self to float along in the sea like some monstrous *ex voto*, arms in the air, feet in the drink and his pants threatening to burst any minute from the weight of the gold. Yet he never regretted for an instant that he had not chosen another profession. He didn't doubt for a moment that he would make port safely.

The people on shore, at the sight of this enraptured creature, his arms rising out of the sea, responded with a truly human gesture. They launched a boat full of husky young fellows. Money doesn't talk. But it smells, it attracts.

The boat, solidly tied to shore by the strapping rescuer's rope, drove boldly out into the raging sea to meet the Saint. When they reached him he was completely exhausted, but he didn't faint.

"Pass over the relics," someone said.

"Never," he shouted. "I've sworn it."

They respected his oath.

All's well that ends well.

Yves Thériault

Akua Nuten

Yves Thériault is one of the heavyweights of Quebec fiction. He has over thirty titles to his credit and when he is in stride produces four or five books a year. Many of them are admittedly potboilers, but others, particularly his evocations of Indian and Eskimo life such as *Ashini*, *Agaguk* and *N'tsuk* are strong elemental tales, like this one taken from his second collection of short stories, *Si la bombe m'était contée* (1962).

Thériault has no fear of the obvious. His heroes, like Kakatso, are simple, strong and long-suffering. His villains lack subtlety. His irony is heavy-fisted. But the power of his tales lies in their sheer narrative drive and rugged authenticity.

Howard Roiter, the translator of this story, is a Montrealer who teaches Canadian and American literature at l'Université de Montréal. He has published frequent articles on Quebec letters in the Toronto *Globe and Mail* and in many periodicals, French and English, American and Canadian. He has just finished a book of criticism entitled *The Modern Canadian Novel.*

Akua Nuten

(The South Wind)

Kakatso, the
Montagnais Indian,
felt the gentle flow of
the air and noticed that
the wind came from the
south. Then he touched the moving water in the
stream to determine the temperature in the
highlands. Since everything pointed to nice June weather, with mild
sunshine and light winds, he decided to go to the highest peak of the
reserve, as he had been planning to do for the past week. There the
Montagnais lands bordered those of the Waswanipis.

There was no urgent reason for the trip. Nothing really pulled him
there except the fact that he hadn't been for a long time; and he liked
steep mountains and frothy, roaring streams.

Three days before he had explained his plan to his son, the thin
Grand-Louis, who was well known to the white men of the North
Shore. His son had guided many whites in the regions surrounding
the Manicouagan and Bersimis rivers.

He had told him: "I plan to go way out, near the limits of the
reserve."

This was clear enough, and Grand-Louis had simply nodded his
head. Now he wouldn't worry, even if Kakatso disappeared for two
months. He would know that his father was high in the hills, breathing the clean air and soaking up beautiful scenes to remember in
future days.

Just past the main branch of the Manicouagan there is an enormous rock crowned by two pines and a fir tree which stand side by
side like the fingers of a hand, the smallest on the left and the others
reaching higher.

This point, which Kakatso could never forget, served as his sign-
post for every trail in the area; and other points would guide him
north, west, or in any other direction. Kakatso, until his final breath,

would easily find his way about there, guided only by the memory of a certain tree, the silhouette of the mountain outlined against the clear skies, the twisting of a river bed, or the slope of a hill.

In strange territory Kakatso would spend entire days precisely organizing his memories so that if he ever returned no trail there would be unknown to him.

Thus, knowing every winding path and every animal's accustomed lair, he could set out on his journey carrying only some salt, tea, and shells for his rifle. He could live by finding his subsistence in the earth itself and in nature's plenty.

Kakatso knew well what a man needed for total independence: a fish-hook wrapped in paper, a length of supple cord, a strong knife, waterproof boots, and a well-oiled rifle. With these things a man could know the great joy of not having to depend on anyone but himself, of wandering as he pleased one day after another, proud and superior, the owner of eternal lands that stretched beyond the horizon.

(To despise the reserve and those who belonged there. Not to have any allegiance except a respect for the water, the sky, and the winds. To be a man, but a man according to the Indian image and not that of the whites. The Indian image of a real man was ageless and changeless, a true image of man in the bosom of a wild and immense nature.)

Kakatso had a wife and a house and grown-up children whom he rarely saw. He really knew little about them. One daughter was a nurse in a white man's city, another had married a turncoat Montagnais who lived in Baie-Comeau and worked in the factories. A son studied far away, in Montreal, and Kakatso would probably never see him again. A son who would repudiate everything, would forget the proud Montagnais language and change his name to be accepted by the whites in spite of his dark skin and slitty eyes.

The other son, Grand-Louis . . . but this one was an exception. He had inherited Montagnais instincts. He often came down to the coast, at Godbout or Sept-Iles, or sometimes at Natashquan, because he was ambitious and wanted to earn money. But this did not cause him to scorn or detest the forest. He found a good life there. For Kakatso, it was enough that this child, unlike so many others, did not turn into a phony white man.

As for Katatso's wife, she was still at home, receiving Kakatso on his many returns without emotion or gratitude. She had a roof over her head, warmth, and food. With skilled fingers she made caribou skin jackets for the white man avid for the exotic. This small sideline liberated Kakatso from other obligations towards her. Soon after returning home, Kakatso always wanted to get away again. He was uncomfortable in these white men's houses that were too high, too solid, and too neatly organized for his taste.

So Kakatso lived his life in direct contact with the forest, and he nurtured life itself from the forest's plenty. Ten months of the year he roamed the forest trails, ten months he earned his subsistence from hunting, trapping, fishing, and smoking the caribou meat that he placed in caches for later use. With the fur pelts he met his own needs and those of the house on the reserve near the forest, although these needs were minimal because his wife was a good earner.

He climbed, then, towards the northern limits of the Montagnais lands on this June day, which was to bring calamity of which he was completely unaware.

Kakatso had heard of the terrible bomb. For twenty years he had heard talk of it, and the very existence of these horrendous machines was not unknown to him. But how was he to know the complex fabric of events happening in the world just then? He never read the newspapers and never really listened to the radio when he happened to spend some hours in a warm house. How could he conceive of total annihilation threatening the whole world? How could he feel all the world's people trembling?

In the forest's vast peace, Kakatso, knowing nature's strength, could easily believe that nothing and nobody could prevail against the mountains, the rivers, and the forest itself stretching out all across the land. Nothing could prevail against the earth, the unchangeable soil that regenerated itself year after year.

He travelled for five days. On the fifth evening it took Kakatso longer to fall asleep. Something was wrong. A silent anguish he did not understand was disturbing him.

He had lit his evening fire on a bluff covered with soft moss, one hundred feet above the lake. He slept there, rolled in his blanket in a deeply dark country interrupted only by the rays of the new moon.

Sleep was slow and when it came it did not bring peace. A jumble of snarling creatures and swarming, roaring masses invaded Kakatso's sleep. He turned over time and again, groaning restlessly. Suddenly he awoke and was surprised to see that the moon had gone down and the night's blackness was lit only by stars. Here, on the bluff, there was a bleak reflection from the sky, but the long valley and the lake remained dark. Exhausted by his throbbing dreams, Kakatso got up, stretched his legs and lit his pipe. On those rare occasions when his sleep was bad he had always managed to recover his tranquillity by smoking a bit, motionless in the night, listening to the forest sounds.

Suddenly the light came. For a single moment the southern and western horizons were illuminated by this immense bluish gleam that loomed up, lingered a moment, and then went out. The dark became even blacker and Kakatso muttered to himself. He wasn't afraid because fear had always been totally foreign to him. But what did this strange event mean? Was it the anger of some old mountain spirit?

All at once the gleam reappeared, this time even more westerly. Weaker this time and less evident. Then the shadows again enveloped the land.

Kakatso no longer tried to sleep that night. He squatted, smoking his pipe and trying to find some explanation for these bluish gleams with his simple ideas, his straightforward logic and vivid memory.

When the dawn came the old Montagnais, the last of his people, the great Abenakis, carefully prepared his fire and boiled some water for his tea.

For some hours he didn't feel like moving. He no longer heard the inner voices calling him to the higher lands. He felt stuck there, incapable of going further until the tumult within him died down. What was there that he didn't know about his skies, he who had spent his whole life wandering in the woods and sleeping under the stars? The sky over his head was as familiar to him as the soil of the underbrush, the animal trails and the games of the trout in their streams. But never before had he seen such gleams and they disturbed him.

At eight o'clock the sun was slowly climbing into the sky, and Kakatsuo was still there.

At ten he moved to the shore to look at the water in the lake. He saw a minnow run and concluded that the lake had many fish. He then attached his fire cord to the hook tied with partridge feathers he had found in the branches of a wild hawthorn bush. He cast the fly with a deliberate, almost solemn movement and it jumped on the smooth water. After Kakatso cast three more times a fat trout swallowed the hook and he pulled him in gently, quite slowly, letting him fight as much as he wanted. The midday meal was in hand. The Montagnais, still in no great hurry to continue his trip, began to prepare his fish.

He was finishing when the far-away buzz of a plane shook him out of his reveries. Down there, over the mountains around the end of the lake, a plane was moving through the sky. This was a familiar sight to Kakatso because all this far country was visited only by planes that landed on the lakes. In this way the Indian had come to know the white man. This was the most frequent place of contact between the two: a large body of quiet water where a plane would land, where the whites would ask for help and find nothing better than an Indian to help them.

Even from a distance Kakatso recognized the type of plane. It was a single-engine, deluxe Bonanza, a type often used by the Americans who came to fish for their salmon in our rivers.

The plane circled the lake and flew over the bluff where Kakatso's fire was still burning. Then it landed gently, almost tenderly. The still waters were only lightly ruffled and quickly returned to their mirror smoothness. The plane slowed down, the motor coughed once or twice, then the craft made a complete turn and headed for the beach.

Kakatso, with one hand shading his eyes, watched the landing, motionless.

When the plane was finally still and the tips of its pontoons were pulled up on the sandy beach, two men, a young woman, and a twelve-year-old boy got out.

One of the men was massive. He towered a head over Kakatso although the Montagnais himself was rather tall.

"Are you an Indian?" the man asked suddenly.

Kakatso nodded slowly and blinked his eyes once.

"Good, I'm glad, you can save us," said the man.

"Save you?" said Kakatso. "Save you from what?"

"Never mind," said the woman, "that's our business."

Standing some distance away, she gestured to the big man who had first spoken to Kakatso.

"If you're trying to escape the police," said Kakatso, "I can't do anything for you."

"It has nothing to do with the police," said the other man who had not spoken previously.

He moved towards Kakatso and proffered a handshake. Now that he was close the Montagnais recognized a veteran bush pilot. His experience could be seen in his eyes, in the squint of his eyelids, and in the way he treated an Indian as an equal.

"I am Bob Ledoux," the man said. "I am a pilot. Do you know what nuclear war is?"

"Yes," answered Kakatso, "I know."

"All the cities in the south have been destroyed," said Ledoux. "We were able to escape."

"Is that a real one?" asked the boy, who had been closely scrutinizing Kakatso. "Eh, Mom, is it really one of those savages?"

"Yes," answered the woman, "certainly." And to Kakatso she said, "Please excuse him. He has never been on the North Shore."

Naturally Kakatso did not like to be considered a savage. But he didn't show anything and he swallowed his bitterness.

"So," said the pilot, "here we are without resources."

"I have money," said the man.

"This is Mr. Perron," said the pilot, "Mrs. Perron, and their son. . . ."

"My name is Roger," said the boy. "I know how to swim."

The Montagnais was still undecided. He did not trust intruders. He preferred, in his simple soul, to choose his own objectives and decide his day's activities. And here were outsiders who had fallen from the sky, almost demanding his help . . . but what help?

"I can't do much for you," he said after a while.

"I have money," the man repeated.

Kakatso shrugged. Money? Why money? What would it buy up here?

Without flinching he had heard how all the southern cities had been destroyed. Now he understood the meaning of those sudden gleams that lit the horizon during the night. And because this event had been the work of whites, Kakatso completely lost interest in it.

So his problem remained these four people he considered spoilers.

"Without you," said the woman, "we are going to perish."

And because Kakatso looked at her in surprise, she added, in a somewhat different tone: "We have no supplies at all and we are almost out of fuel."

"That's true," said the pilot.

"So," continued the woman, "if you don't help us find food, we will die."

Kakatso, with a sweeping gesture, indicated the forests and the lake: "There is wild game there and fish in the waters. . . ."

"I don't have a gun or fishhooks," said the pilot. "And it's been a very long time since I came so far north."

He said this with a slightly abashed air and Kakatso saw clearly that the man's hands were too white; the skin had become too soft and smooth.

"I'll pay you whatever is necessary," said Mr. Perron.

"Can't you see," said his wife, "that money doesn't interest him?"

Kakatso stood there, looking at them with his shining impassive eyes, his face unsmiling and his arms dangling at his sides.

"Say something," cried the woman. "Will you agree to help us?"

"We got away as best we could," said the pilot. "We gathered the attack on Montreal was coming and we were already at the airport when the warning sirens went off. But I couldn't take on enough fuel. There were other planes leaving too. I can't even take off again from this lake. Do you know if there is a supply cache near here?"

Throughout the northern forests pilots left emergency fuel caches for use when necessary. But if Kakatso knew of several such places he wasn't letting on in front of the intruders.

"I don't know," he said.

There was silence.

The whites looked at the Indian and desperately sought words to persuade him. But Kakatso did not move and said nothing. He had always fled the society of whites and dealt with them only when it was unavoidable. Why should he treat those who surfaced here now any differently? They were without food; the forest nourishes those who know how to take their share. This knowledge was such an instinctive part of an Indian's being that he couldn't realize how some people could lack it. He was sure that these people wanted to impose their needs on him and enslave him. All his Montagnais pride revolted against this thought. And yet, he could help them. Less than one hour away there was one of those meat caches of a thousand pounds of smoked moose, enough to see them through a winter. And the fish in the lake could be caught without much effort. Weaving a simple net of fine branches would do it, or a trap of bulrushes.

But he didn't move a muscle.

Only a single fixed thought possessed Kakatso, and it fascinated him. Down there, in the south, the whites had been destroyed. Never again would they reign over these forests. In killing each other, they had rid the land of their kind. Would the Indians be free again? All the Indians, even those on the reserves? Free to retake the forests?

And these four whites: could they be the last survivors?

Brothers, thought Kakatso, all my brothers: it is up to me to protect your new freedom.

"The cities," he finally said, "they have really been destroyed?"

"Yes," said the pilot.

"Nothing is left any more," said the woman. "Nothing at all. We saw the explosion from the plane. It was terrible. And the wind pushed us for a quarter of an hour. I thought we were going to crash."

"Nothing left," said the boy, "nobody left. Boom! One bomb did it."

He was delighted to feel himself the hero—a safe and sound hero —of such an adventure. He didn't seem able to imagine the destruction and death, only the spectacular explosion.

But the man called Perron had understood it well. He had been able to estimate the real power of the bomb.

"The whole city is destroyed," he said. "A little earlier, on the radio, we heard of the destruction of New York, then Toronto and Ottawa. . . ."

"Many other cities too," added the pilot. "As far as I'm concerned, nothing is left of Canada, except perhaps the North Shore. . . ."

"And it won't be for long," said Perron. "If we could get further up, further north. If we only had food and gasoline."

This time he took a roll of money out of his pocket and unfolded five bills, a sum Kakatso had never handled at one time. Perron offered them to the Indian.

"Here. The only thing we ask you for is a little food and gas if you can get some. Then we could leave."

"When such a bomb explodes," said Kakatso without taking the bills, "does it kill all the whites?"

"Yes," said the pilot. "In any case, nearly all."

"One fell on Ottawa?"

"Yes."

"Everybody is dead there?"

"Yes. The city is small and the bomb was a big one. The reports indicate there were no survivors."

Kakatso nodded his head two or three times approvingly. Then he turned away and took his rifle which had been leaning on a rock. *37 + Akua Nuten*

Slowly, aiming at the whites, he began to retreat into the forest.

"Where are you going?" cried the woman.

"Here," said the man. "Here's all my money. Come back!"

Only the pilot remained silent. With his sharp eyes he watched Kakatso.

When the Indian reached the edge of the forest it was the boy's turn. He began to sob pitifully, and the woman also began to cry.

"Don't leave," she cried. "Please, help us. . . ."

For all of my people who cried, thought Kakatso, all who begged, who wanted to defend their rights for the past two hundred years: I take revenge for them all.

But he didn't utter another word.

And when the two men wanted to run after him to stop him, he put his rifle to his shoulder. The bullet nicked the pilot's ear. Then the men understood that it would be futile to insist, and Kakatso disappeared into the forest which enclosed him. Bent low, he skimmed the ground, using every bush for cover, losing himself in the undergrowth, melting into the forest where he belonged.

Later, having circled the lake, he rested on a promontory hidden behind many spreading cedars. He saw that the pilot was trying to take off to find food elsewhere.

But the tanks were nearly empty and when the plane reached an altitude of a thousand feet the motor sputtered a bit, backfired and stopped.

The plane went into a nosedive.

When it hit the trees it caught fire.

In the morning Kakatso continued his trip towards the highlands.

He felt his first nausea the next day and vomited blood two days later. He vomited once at first, then twice, then a third time, and finally one last time.

The wind kept on blowing from the south, warm and mild.

Gérard Bessette

The Mustard Plaster

Gérard Bessette, scholar, teacher and novelist, perhaps because of his long association with Queen's University, Kingston, is one of the rare Quebec writers to have found a translator to match his own considerable talents. The late Glen Shortliffe translated his second novel, *Le Libraire* (1960) as *Not For Every Eye* in 1962 and his fourth, *Incubation* (1967), with wit and accuracy.

Bessette's satirical attacks on middle-class prudery and hypocrisy made him an avant-garde writer in the late 'fifties. He has continued to expose narrowness and provincialism from his exile's vantage point in novels like *Le Cycle* (1971) and in stories like "The Mustard Plaster". His rasping, insistent, semi-pedestrian realism is well captured in the story that follows.

Anthony Robinow has done translations of plays by Gratien Gélinas, Marcel Dubé and Eloi de Grandmont for the Théâtre du Nouveau Monde. He has also worked for the CBC, the NFB, and Potterton Productions as actor, scriptwriter and producer and now runs his own film company, Robinow Productions.

The Mustard Plaster

The old man slammed
the door behind him.
His wrinkled face
was livid, and his lips
quivered with rage.
Grasping his cane firmly in one bony hand,
he started down the stairs. *They'll never see me again. It's all over.* At
each step he had to feel in front of him with the cane, like a mole
dazzled by daylight. No longer would they insult him, or make fun of
his advice, or ignore his eighty years of experience. *I shall never give
in.* From now on their promises and sweet talk would fall on deaf
ears. After all, they were the ones who had begged him to come and
live with them. ("You'll see. You'll be just fine. We have a beautiful big
room waiting for you.") *The hypocrites! It was because of my pension of
course. If only Léon hadn't brought that great big Englishwoman back from
Europe after the war....* The old man had never quite been able to
accept the fact that Shirley, that stranger who didn't even speak
French, was his daughter-in-law.

On his return to Canada, Léon had naturally found himself un-
employed. He'd never been much good at making his own way. And
because he had been a lieutenant during the war, he had imagined
that a lucrative job would be his for the asking. While waiting for this
to happen, he "put out feelers", looking for "something suitable,
something worthy of his talents...." His veteran's allowance ran out
before he found anything. And at that point he and Shirley had re-
doubled their insistence that Mr. Denaud should come and live with
them. And the old man had agreed. They had been living together
for about five years now. Léon had eventually had to take back his
old job as a cashier in a bank. And at the end of every month, in
addition to the generous rent he already paid them, Mr. Denaud was
obliged to give them a little extra to keep the household solvent.
Shirley had no sense of the value of money, or of how to keep to a

budget. The moment she got her hands on a few dollars, she wasted them on extravagances. *What a fool I've been!* He should have left them earlier, when he was stronger and could see more clearly. *Never mind. Better late than never.*

Testing the surface by tapping his cane before him like the antenna of an insect, the old man advanced along the sidewalk with small, careful steps. A fall would be catastrophic, for he knew he would never be able to get up again without help. Since he was well-known in the neighbourhood, he would be taken back to the house; or, worse still, someone would go and get Léon. This had happened four or five times during the last few months. Recently, Mr. Denaud had suffered inexplicable momentary blackouts which he had not admitted to a soul, but which made things spin around him in a dizzying nightmare. *I really should make up my mind to go and see a doctor.* The thought occurred to him, but he had plenty of other things to occupy his mind. Didn't he have to find another place to live, to have his things moved, his furniture? He grinned at the thought. Once his furniture was removed, Léon's place would be pretty empty. Mr. Denaud imagined Shirley's stricken expression on seeing her almost empty rooms. What, in fact, would be left? A stove, a table, three or four chairs, a bed, and that's about all. The sofa in the living-room? *Yes, obviously I shall have to leave them the sofa.* Young Richard slept on it, and Mr. Denaud could not take it away from them—especially now that the little boy was ill. It was, in fact, because of that. . . . The old man swallowed painfully. He didn't want to think about that for the moment. The difficulties of walking, and the unevenness of the sidewalk took all his attention.

Mr. Denaud reached Sherbrooke Street, which, at this point, seemed as wide as a river. The thought of crossing it terrified him. Beads of sweat stood out on his wrinkled forehead. Cars rushed by at ridiculous speeds and with deafening roars from their exhausts. He would have to cross this vast space with no other guidelines than the two faded white strips that marked the pedestrian crossing. The old man could not trust the traffic lights. He saw them out of focus as diffuse globes of light that blended with the adjacent red and green neon sign of a drugstore. Mr. Denaud always avoided this dangerous intersection on his daily walks. He would go four blocks further along, where a safety island allowed him to cross the street in two stages. But what would happen now if he had a dizzy spell in the middle of the traffic? His throat was dry, his eyes were smarting.

Today he could not indulge in his customary detour. He would have to save his energy. *Of course, I could always ask a passer-by to help me.* But he rejected that possibility. It would have been an admission of failure, of his dependence on Léon and Shirley that he was unable to shake off. This reflection gave him courage. He waited until the stream of traffic in the cross-street started across Sherbrooke, then set out across the road himself, walking as fast as he could and tapping with his cane.

By the time he reached the far side he was bathed in sweat. There was a throbbing in his ears and he had to lean against the drugstore window to catch his breath again. Only then did he wonder where he was going. Until that moment he had thought only of escaping, of getting away as quickly as possible. Conflicting possibilities made his head spin. Nevertheless, a decision would have to be reached. *But not here. I can't decide anything here.* He would have to find a place to sit down, to relax and reflect. He set off again towards Ontario Street, using his cane to counteract the steep incline of the sidewalk. *Where shall I go?* The Ladies of St. Edward Club, where, from time to time, he met a few cronies? *No, if I go there they'll make fun of me.* They would question him, old man Chartier especially, and he would end up making "a clean breast of it", and telling them all the details of the argument with Léon and Shirley. Chartier also lived with his son. *Poor old Chartier!* Every month he had to hand over his entire old-age pension to his son, without a murmur, so afraid was he of being sent to an old people's home. *I'd be in the same fix if I hadn't managed to put away some savings.* No, the club was out of the question. Besides, he would not see his pals again now. He was going to start again from scratch, a totally new life. But where was he to go in the meantime? A restaurant, perhaps? No good: he wasn't hungry. Anxiety lay like a weight on his stomach. Besides, tea or coffee gave him palpitations, and carbonated drinks gave him heartburn. Of course, he could always order something and then not drink it, but such waste was unacceptable to a man of his strict and parsimonious habits. He had so often reproached Léon and Shirley for their extravagances that he could hardly fall into the same trap himself!

While deliberating he reached Ontario Street. Once more he was covered in sweat. He felt worn out and weak. He took a few more faltering steps when his nostrils were assailed by the smell of malt and yeast which a large ventilator was blowing across the sidewalk. A glass of beer might do him some good. There was a humming in his ears, and he was only vaguely aware of his surroundings as he wandered into the tavern, stumbled into another patron—who continued on his way, muttering insults—and collapsed into a chair by a small white table. At last he could rest and collect his thoughts. No doubt a tavern was not the ideal place. And, indeed, Mr. Denaud had not been inside one for years. His father, many years before, had been in the habit of knocking back rather more than was wise, and of coming home somewhat the worse for wear of a Friday evening, when he would shout down the recriminations of Mr. Denaud's mother. But that had all been so long ago it no longer had any meaning. He, Mr. Denaud, was now an octogenarian, a widower without a family, so to speak, since Léon no longer counted, and since his daughter, Adèle, had married an American and lived in Miami.

The old man swallowed some beer. There were those who said it was good for the health. According to old Chartier, it stimulated the circulation. And surely dizzy spells were caused by defective circulation? Mr. Denaud remembered having read this information in some medical article. He wiped his moustache with the back of his hand, feeling better. *My Dad died at ninety-five. He never had dizzy spells. And he drank his daily half-dozen bottles of beer.* But he put these thoughts out of his mind. It was not his health that was at issue. A much more urgent problem had to be dealt with: the question of finding somewhere to live, and arranging to have his things moved.

He sighed and gazed around the room through watery eyes. At a neighbouring table two men were drinking and discussing the race track news. One of them had won 350 dollars the day before, and was jubilant. The other had not had any luck and the two horses he bet on had finished among the last. He spoke with a lazy drawl like Léon's. Mr. Denaud took another swallow. And then the circumstances that had led up to his leaving the house struck him with unusual force and clarity for a man whose memory of recent events was inclined to be hazy.

The drama, for that is what it had been, had started with his grandson Richard's illness. No wonder the child had fallen ill. Time and again the old man had warned Shirley not to let him sleep in a room with an open window. She, of course, simply did what she felt like doing. She insisted it was good for his health. And, of course, it hadn't been long before the little one caught a cold and began to cough. And still the window remained open. The old man had had violent arguments with his daughter-in-law. He had even warned her that the boy's lungs were inflamed. He might as well have saved his breath. By the time she finally got around to calling the doctor, Richard had a temperature of a hundred and four.

Mr. Denaud took a gulp of beer, and dabbed at his moustache with his handkerchief. Beside him, the two men were still discussing horses and the pari-mutuels. New customers were drifting into the tavern and there was a buzz of conversation. From the very first sign that he was ill, what that little kid had needed was a mustard plaster. Mr. Denaud had recommended it to Shirley, and to Léon. And they had made fun of him, saying that it was an old-fashioned, a prehistoric remedy! Nowadays it was all penicillin, oleomycin, antihistamines and things like that—all of them worthless inventions for taking away poor people's money. Mushroom mould for curing an inflammation of the lungs! What was the world coming to? And the doctors and the druggists kept getting richer. Well, then, one simply had to protest. But when the old man tried to intervene, the young doctor had practically ordered him to mind his own business. And, as usual, Mr. Denaud had had to pay for the prescription because Léon had been broke.

With a sigh he raised his glass once more. A waiter asked him if he wanted another and without thinking he nodded his assent. *These young doctors nowadays are a bunch of incompetent hotheads.* And the proof was that the penicillin hadn't done any good. After a temporary improvement, Richard's fever had risen to 103.7. And all the time there had been a proven, effective remedy for inflammation of the lungs. The sight of his grandson's red, congested face, as the child twisted and turned in bed, made Mr. Denaud decide to take charge.

Without saying a word to anyone he went off to the corner grocery to buy a box of mustard. He knew all about plasters. Many's the time he'd prepared them in the past. And it was the simplest thing in the world. All you did was make a paste with mustard and water, spread the paste between two pieces of cotton and apply it to the patient's chest. Proud of his shrewdness, Mr. Denaud had quickly slipped into the bathroom with his box of mustard and a thin linen towel. As he prepared the plaster, he wondered whether it might not be a good idea to add a little flour to the mustard to lessen its sting. He vaguely remembered his mother doing something like that when one of the kids was sick. But he didn't have any flour. Should he try and get some from the kitchen? But if he did that, Shirley would be sure to notice, and the whole project would miscarry. *After all, it doesn't really matter.* And he decided only to apply the plaster for about ten minutes.

Still sitting at his table in the tavern, his cane propped against the edge of the table, Mr. Denaud shook his head. Once more he raised his glass to his lips to drown his anger. As long as he had been allowed to do things his own way his project had advanced without any problems. On entering Richard's room he had peered at the alarm clock to see what the time was, and then had applied the mustard plaster. But from that point on things had gone wrong. He had barely put back the covers when Shirley entered the room with a pill and a glass of water in her hand. It was time for the child's medicine. *I should have just let her get on with it and not said a thing,* said Mr. Denaud to himself. But it had been too much for him and he had protested vehemently against these newfangled quacks' remedies. Hadn't the child's temperature gone up again, after all? So why persist with these stupidities? His daughter-in-law had simply shrugged her shoulders and briskly suggested that he mind his own business. Mr. Denaud had been about to reply when, after taking a couple of sniffs, the Englishwoman had remarked that there was "a funny smell" in the room. So saying, she had looked straight at her father-in-law, who had blushed and made a great point of admitting that perhaps in the end she was right about the pills. After all, what did he know about modern drugs? The old man was annoyed to recall how he had humbled himself. *For all the good it did me. . . .*

He looked around the tavern. It was half full. Groups of labourers had dropped in for a drink on their way home. Two men sat down at his table, roaring with laughter. One was almost bald and had a huge strawberry-coloured nose; the other was a sort of dwarf who wore a baseball cap with a plastic visor and chewed a long cigar. Before Mr. Denaud could protest, they had stood him a glass. He drank with them, muttering thanks which they ignored. *If Léon could see me, he wouldn't believe his eyes.* For a moment, the old man wished his son were there so he could tell him that he had no need of him and was perfectly capable of looking after himself. But he rejected this thought which, in itself, was a sign of dependence. *I must put all that sort of thing behind me.* Léon had been as much to blame as Shirley—perhaps even more, in a sense, for after all he was his own son.

The plaster had been on Richard's chest for exactly nine minutes when Léon returned unexpectedly from the office, two hours earlier than usual, just after Shirley had left the room. The old man had been peering at the alarm clock just as the door opened. He started and quickly suppressed an expression of annoyance. Léon rushed into the room still wearing his overcoat. Richard seemed to be dozing. His eyes were closed and the breath whistled gently through his half-open mouth. The little blond head with the flushed face just lay there against the pillow without the slightest movement. Obviously the plaster was beginning to take effect. If only Léon hadn't lingered so long in the room. The old man had become more and more nervous as he watched the minutes go by on the clock. Léon had also noticed the bitter smell in the room. The old man pretended that the smell came from some menthol nose drops, an explanation Léon accepted with a shrug. And finally he had left the room. Mr. Denaud rushed to the bedside at the very moment when Richard woke up suddenly and cried out in pain. Quickly the old man had removed the plaster and, on hearing Shirley's and Léon's footsteps in the corridor outside, had thrown it in desperation into the waste-paper basket. But by now the air was so saturated with the bitter odour of the mustard that there was no point in trying to hide it. Léon had immediately found the plaster in the waste basket, while Shirley had bent over the child's chest and yelled with rage: "He'll kill him! That's what he's going to do! He wants to kill him!"

Apparently the little boy's skin had been covered with yellowish blisters. But Mr. Denaud had seen none of this. He had not been allowed to get close to the child. Besides, would he have been able to see them with his poor myopic eyes? Shirley had become more violent. She had insisted on remaining mistress in her own house. She was not prepared to allow her child to be killed by an old lunatic. And if that didn't happen to suit Mr. Denaud, he had only to leave the house. And Léon had said nothing: he hadn't even protested! His own son.

"You got a light?"

The old man jumped, then turned his head towards the man who had spoken to him. He started going through his pockets, then remembered that he hadn't smoked since he'd started getting those deaf spells.

"No, I'm sorry."

But by this time, the man had turned away to ask someone else. And Mr. Denaud resumed his reflections. "She practically threw me out," he muttered. If, at least, he had left of his own free will he would have felt less bitter.

He finished his glass and continued to sit there, collapsed in his chair with his head slumped down on his chest. His breathing became more difficult, his vision more blurred. *I'm going to have a dizzy spell.* He began to panic. What would become of him, so far from home, in this tavern where nobody knew him? No doubt it was the lack of air; the atmosphere was filled with smoke. *I must get a breath of fresh air outside.*

Grabbing his cane, he got up with difficulty, steadying himself with one pale hand on the enamel surface of the table. After a moment he felt better and risked a few steps. *I'm not all that weak, not that incapable, I. . . .* At that moment his foot struck the leg of a chair. He tried to lean on his cane but it slipped in a puddle of beer. He felt himself falling forward, then a hard object hit his skull near the temple.

When he came to, the waiter was dabbing his forehead with a cold napkin. A warm viscous liquid was trickling down the side of his face.

"Feeling better, Dad?"

The old man nodded weakly, then closed his eyes again.

"Somebody'll have to take him home. Anyone here know him?"

"No, no," murmured Mr. Denaud, "not home."

At the same time he felt a hand going through his pockets and removing his wallet. Were they going to rob him? He made a gesture as if to reclaim his property. But all they had wanted was his address.

"It's not far from here," said a voice. "I'll call a taxi."

"No," said the old man, "I don't want to."

"You're sure not in any shape to walk, Dad," said the waiter. "Go on, take a taxi. That's the best thing to do."

He felt two powerful arms lift him up by the armpits. He made a feeble attempt to free himself but the room, the tables, the walls were spinning. A sudden overwhelming fatigue made him go weak at the knees. *Just to lie down in a bed, anywhere, but just to lie down.* If no one had been supporting him, he would have lost consciousness again and collapsed. He couldn't get the air into his lungs. He breathed with a raucous whistling sound. Someone put his hat back on his head, and he was practically carried to the taxi. Two men sat on either side of him in the back seat of the car. He was barely conscious during the journey. Going up the stairs, still supported by the two men, he belched and his mouth filled with bitter foamy liquid. Then he heard Léon's voice:

"Now what's happened to him? He had to go out by himself, naturally, even though I warned him. There, careful now, we'll put him to bed."

"He was in the tavern," said one of the men. "All of a sudden, there he was stretched out on the floor. Must have hit his head on one of the tables. Look, you can see: it's still bleeding a little."

"What did you say?" It was Shirley's drawling voice. "The tavern? He was in the tavern? That's the limit! If he's going to start drinking, that's all we need! Thank you, thank you very much. We try to keep an eye on him, you know, but today our son was sick, and he slipped away when no one was looking."

"Yeah," said one of the men, "looking after old folks isn't easy. My Dad's like that, too."

The old man made a violent effort to sit up in bed. He was not going to allow such flagrant distortions of the truth without registering a protest. Neither Shirley nor Léon had ever forbidden him to go out. But he only managed to raise his head slightly.

"Would you like some coffee? There's some hot in the kitchen," said Shirley.

The two men declined. Mr. Denaud heard the door closing. It seemed to him he was left alone for ages. *No one looks after me. They wanted to get rid of me. It's me who supports them, and they wanted to get rid of me.* Suddenly he thought of Richard. How could he have forgotten him for such a long time?

"Léon, Léon!" he shouted in a hoarse voice.

Léon came rushing in. "What is it? You're not still in pain?"

The old man felt his heart thumping away in his chest, and he needed a few moments to catch his breath again.

"Richard . . . how is . . . how is he?"

"He's better," said Léon. "The doctor came and gave him an injection. That calmed him."

Mr. Denaud's features relaxed.

"It was the mustard plaster," he announced with some difficulty. "It was the plaster."

"We won't talk about that, please," said Léon. "That's over with."

"It's the plaster, I tell you."

Leon said nothing. The old man's lips formed a smile. His breathing was easier now. *I knew he'd end up on my side. He's just ashamed to admit it, but he knows he was wrong.* Mr. Denaud was filled with intense joy at the thought that because of him Richard was better. It

had hurt him so much to see the little chap suffering, lying in bed with his flushed face swollen with the fever. *It's when they suffer that one realizes just how much one loves them.* The old man closed his eyes, and shook his head. *How could I have even considered the possibility of leaving the little one? How could I have lived without him?* It was unthinkable. After all, it was better to put up with Shirley's sneers. *Shirley . . .* The old man was so proud of having "saved" his grandson that he was prepared to think more kindly of his daughter-in-law. Though she was too proud to admit it, she must be ashamed of her behaviour. And, besides, wasn't she Richard's mother? So was it not she who unwittingly had provided the old man with a reason for living, a consolation for his declining years?

"Léon."

"Yes, Dad?"

"You may tell Shirley that I forgive her."

"That you forgive her? What do you mean?"

"You will tell Shirley that I forgive her," repeated the old man.

He saw Léon shake his head.

"Okay. I'll tell her. You have a rest now."

With a deep sigh of contentment Mr. Denaud closed his eyes. *Life will go on as before. I won't have to move. I'll see the little one every day.* A pleasing warmth spread through him at the thought. With a smile on his lips he saw himself once again applying the mustard plaster that was to cure Richard. *I am still useful. Even Léon didn't dare deny it.* His heart beat more calmly. Slowly and voluptuously he filled his lungs with life-giving air. Then he slipped into peaceful sleep.

Roger Fournier

Jos-la-Fiole

Roger Fournier (b. 1929) is a talented, erratic, irre-
pressible writer and TV producer who has published half
a dozen novels and a book of short stories, *Les Filles à
Mounne* (1966), from which the present selection is
taken.

This anthology would have been incomplete and un-
representative without a story or two from rural Quebec
which, despite the rapid modernization that has transformed the country in the last decade, is still the cultural
backbone of the nation. But how the tone has changed
since *Maria Chapdelaine* and *Trente Arpents*! Roger Fournier's farmers are a far cry from the *habitants* of old, and
there is no pastoral elegizing here, nor any romanticizing
about the merits of life near the soil. In a story like this,
realism and frank laughter replace the traditional rev-
erence for country life and country ways.

Alison d'Anglejan, the translator of this story, is a doctoral candidate working with the Language Research
Group of the Department of Psychology at McGill. Her
research interests centre on problems of bilingualism.

Jos-la-Fiole

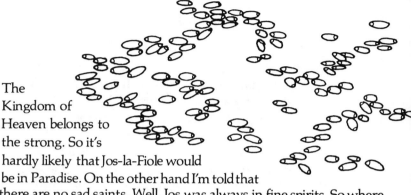

The Kingdom of Heaven belongs to the strong. So it's hardly likely that Jos-la-Fiole would be in Paradise. On the other hand I'm told that there are no sad saints. Well, Jos was always in fine spirits. So where can he possibly be? For this fellow really did exist. His story still makes all his fellow parishioners laugh although it truly is a sad tale. Country folk, one must admit, are a merciless lot.

Jos-la-Fiole's name was actually Joseph Leclerc. But in this fine family the virtues of strong drink had been discovered some generations back and a bottle was always on hand. As a result the entire family had long ago been nicknamed La-Fiole (the flask) on account of the famous bottle, that source of endless merriment. As for the Joseph, well of course it quite naturally became Jos.

For a number of years Jos had worn the same grey felt fedora, a former "Sunday hat" whose band had been replaced by a ring of darkish colour, his own greasy perspiration. One could scarcely see his eyes, his small weasely eyes that seemed to float in a sort of private bliss. His face was slightly twisted on one side; on the other an arm swung loosely like the limb of a marionette; and he leaned a little on the opposite leg which seemed to be the weaker of the two. In spite of this ungainliness Jos-la-Fiole's bearing was fairly harmonious, each defect balancing out another. When he walked his entire organism fell into that flexible kind of motion that betrays a gentle nature.

Jos must have found his happiness within himself, probably even in his own weakness. For neither his wife, nor his land, nor his children could offer him any. Twice his height and weight, Jos' wife was a sort of dejected "heavyweight", trailing about the house in a drab dress and shapeless slippers. She milked the cows in silence, only moaning a little when the animal's tail, in search of flies, slapped her squarely in the eye. Naturally gloomy, she had easily adapted to her husband's slovenly ways and had become even more sloppy than he was. But it never occurred to either to criticize the other.

Jos had two fairly grown-up sons but they had no love for the land. So they worked indifferently at seeding and haying, and then when harvest time came around they were off to the lumber camps up north where there was money to be made. They would return at Easter with long beards and full pockets and would make their offering to the god of drink along with the rest of the La-Fioles.

As for his land, it wasn't very successful either. It was located on the fourth concession where stones abound and the dry slopes forever seem to have been seeded with thistles and "devil's paint brush". Good year, bad year, Jos harvested no more than four or five times his amount of seed, but he was no worse off for that: Jos-la-Fiole didn't know how to complain.

Now don't go thinking that to keep happy he got drunk every day! No, but such occasions did arise. For instance, on certain Sundays when his neighbour, Edgar Beaulieu, was having an evening. Jos would see the cars and buggies drawing up around the house. He would hear the music of the violins in the cool of the evening. Then the simple joy of the two-step rhythm would begin to dance in his heart and visions of women's calves and bosoms to leap before his eyes. Eventually he would make up his mind to hop the fence and join the festivities. By the time he got there several jugs would already be empty, making everyone affable, and he would be welcomed with open bottles. He would then drink his share of happiness and watch the young people dancing.

There were also the great religious feast days that had to be celebrated lavishly if Christ's stay on earth was not to be forgotten. For Jos-la-Fiole days of birth and death were feasted, as well as days of great surprises, special events, or other unusual happenings. This furnished a happily balanced calendar, providing him with fairly frequent oases along his arid path.

No one knew quite how, but Monsieur le Curé was aware of all these celebrations. He was a very wise and gentle priest but the abuse of "inebriating drink" on religious feast days, and especially at those Sunday "evenings", he viewed as vulgar debauchery. The will of God was indeed that we should think of him on the seventh day. In his sermon at high mass, Monsieur le Curé returned to this topic nearly every month:

"Brethren, I ask you to pray for the souls of some among us. In certain parts of the parish there are those who seem to forget that happiness is not of this world and who seek to find it in pleasure. I am not preaching against entertainment, healthy entertainment. But brethren, do you truly believe that inebriating drink and modern dancing are healthy entertainment? (He always spoke softly.) Do you never think about the fact that the virtue of young women, and even of married women, is threatened when they lose their heads through the use of alcohol? Brethren, as I have said before many times, your spiritual life is like having a new car. If you try to drive it in a state of inebriation you are bound to have an accident one day, and you will destroy everything. . . ."

He continued in these homely tones for a few more minutes, trying to reach the hearts of his children from the heights of the pulpit. The parishioners knew very well to whom he was alluding, and the village busybodies took this opportunity to chuckle smugly in their beards (such women always have a few whiskers) at the thought of the high esteem Monsieur le Curé must have for them, since he could see them in church every day. As for those poor souls from the fourth concession, they felt all eyes upon them like so many reproaches from God himself. They repented to the best of their ability, even Jos-la-Fiole. Especially Jos, for he was the weakest of them all. But just as he was the weakest when faced with the chiding of Monsieur le Curé, so he was also when faced with temptation. As a result he felt great joy rising from the depths of his soul when he was handed a bottle, promptly forgot about the "beautiful car of spiritual life", and enjoyed himself down to the last glass.

A few years ago, because my father was the only one to own a separator capable of threshing clover and millet as well as grain, he used to "thrash" for everyone in the parish and even for some outsiders. In our part of the country the hay seed ripens around the beginning of August, just before the grain. This meant that near the middle of the month there was always a crowd out at our place: they came "to have their crop thrashed". (There are some things you have to resign yourself to.) I liked this time of year because it let me get a closer look at people I normally saw only from a distance, at Sunday mass or in the fields. One unusual thing I noticed each year was that these men were always in fine spirits. (Apart from the members of a certain family who were never known to laugh, but then their father died a madman, you see.) Generally in good health, the farmers around us derived a simple pleasure from coming over to have their grain threshed.

"Whooaoh! Whooaoh!" This loud cry shouted at the top of their lungs announced their arrival at the barn, each man standing on his load of ripe hay. Oh August sun just beginning to wane! Oh summer wind carrying the sound of the two-stroke engine that drove the separator for hours and hours without tiring: it was you who gave me those idyllic days that I have known nowhere else! The entire barn shook with the vibrations of the machine and through the great open doors rolled clouds of black dust that filled the lungs. But wherever there's a harvest there's joy to be found.

One especially beautiful day when there was prosperity and happiness in the air, Jos-la-Fiole appeared perched up on a load that was too much for his poor dun mare. He was greeted with jibes as plain and direct as the farmers who made them:

"Hey! Ti-Jos, don't tell me ya grew all that hay in just one crop!"

That was Willy, sure of himself as always, sticking his big nose into everything. Because of his strong voice he did the calling at the village auctions.

"Yer mare's pissin' water, Jos! An' she's skinny as a rake. Ya never had no oats ta give her I s'pose."

That was Ernest, one of the richest farmers in the region whose great red cheeks matched his lethargy. Ernest seemed as sure of everything as he was sure of his splendid team of black horses.

Jos-la-Fiole chose not to reply. He laughed in his usual good-natured way, even a little harder than usual, revealing the white false teeth he was so proud of. To him this was a big day for he was sure to be named champion of the year for his grain. Indeed, the season had been rainy and his dry slopes had profited from it, whereas the great damp bottomlands of the others had suffered. He had almost come to believe in miracles that year, seeing his miserable slopes covered with red clover. Actually there wasn't that much of it, but for him it was "heaven on earth". So he had selected the finest patch and let it ripen, telling himself he would dazzle everyone at threshing time.

It soon became noticeable that he was laughing more than necessary. Jos was celebrating the goodness of providence which had given him lots of rain and a fine crop of clover. My father appeared at the hayloft door, black with dust and spitting out whatever dirt his lungs couldn't handle. As soon as he caught sight of Jos-la-Fiole a look of annoyance came over his face. It was the same old story every year: all you ever got from the fourth concession was loads of couch grass and thistles. Since he was paid according to pounds of seed threshed, he wasted both time and money with them.

"Greetings Fleurien!" said Jos-la-Fiole jauntily to my father. "What do you think of my clover seed? Betcha never seen any better."

"Well now! Let's have a look."

He moved closer to the load, surprised at first by the abundance and size of the spikes of clover the sun had blackened. He picked up two or three and crushed them in his hand with a quick circular motion of his thumb.

"My poor Jos, your seed's already been threshed by plant lice."

"What!"

Jos-la-Fiole could feel himself about to sober up. So he got out his bottle of hootch and downed a few good mouthfuls.

"See, look at that," said my father. "Don't tell me you don't know what clover lice are?"

And he showed him with the tip of his nail the treacherous little black dots that were sauntering around the heart of the clover spike as though they were at home in their own front parlour. Jos hiccupped and his jaw remained clenched for a few seconds. He hadn't thought to have a close look at his clover before letting it ripen.

"Damn!"

For the first time in his life he would have been able to show off a nice sackful of seed from his own slopes, his poor slopes that everyone made fun of even to his face. For the first time he might have been proud of his land, the land that was beginning to daunt him with its dryness. Had he not been accustomed to a certain measure of misery he might have started to weep. But he decided to believe that there was plenty of seed in his load and he replied to my father:

"Come on, Fleurien, ya know full well that them there little bugs couldn't eat their way through my whole load of hay! Come on, come on, we'll thresh it and you'll see what'll come out of your machine."

Nobody dared say a word but everyone there realized that Jos-la-Fiole's courage was as great as the sun, as long as the autumn rains, and as tough as winter. There was nothing Fleurien could do but agree to this hour of futile work.

"You could at least offer a man a drink," said my father. And once more Jos pulled out his bottle.

Jos' face was happy again as he got ready to pitch off his load. His usual high spirits had returned and he plunged his fork with every ounce of his slight strength into the musty hay which landed on the floor with a rustling sound. When the wagon had been emptied of its precious load it was driven down alongside the ramp to take on the threshed hay. The engine started up, clattering with all the might of its six horsepower, while the assembly of belts and pulleys on the great red beast began to turn. Things went well. My father ran the separator and it was Jos himself who fed in his small forkloads. To help out, Willy gathered up the threshed hay which he threw into the wagon over beside the ramp. As anticipated, the lice had done much of the threshing and there was little seed left over. But our friend had already accepted this, consoling himself with the fact that for once the hay at least had been good.

There were no further incidents, except that big Willy, seeing Jos' mare each trip he made to the wagon, noticed that she was in heat. Now in those days my father kept a superb stallion to attend to the needs of the farm (and to add to his own troubles, for the animal was as frisky as the devil and had broken four or five carts over the past few years). Since the stallion was in the stable and the mare not far away, they could smell each other and their whinnying drowned out even the noise of the engine. Willy was the only one who knew why, since he had seen the mare pissing more than usual in a way that could only mean one thing.

When the whole load had been put through the thresher the men went out into the fresh air, their faces black with dust and sweat, to have a look at the few pounds of seed that had been collected. Willy came up and said with an almost childlike smile:

"Listen Jos, d'ya know yer mare's in heat?"

"That so? Ah, the slut!"

Everything came to a halt for a moment while all eyes fixed on my father. They knew the stallion was in the stable and that he wanted nothing better than to satisfy the poor mare. My father was thinking to himself that it was unwise to let the thing happen in front of witnesses for his stallion was not registered, and if he was reported it would cost him a fat fine. In the end, Willy summed up what everyone was thinking:

"Go ahead, Fleurien, we won't say a word."

Jos-la-Fiole placed the last weight on the scale and said with the air of a child martyr:

"You understand, it would be some consolation for that little bit of seed I got. I'd be that much to the good. . . ."

Undoubtedly, since it would have cost him ten dollars to have his mare serviced by a registered stud. Since they were all eager to see the animal "have a go" they swore silence and my father started towards the stable. The stallion had already got his guns into position, excited by the smell of the mare which he was inhaling deeply, his lips drawn back, teeth bared, head pointing to the ceiling.

Outside the "blonde" was being stripped of her harness and her nakedness was presented to the lord of the harem impatiently pawing the ground in the passage. Since the stable door was cut in two, enabling the bottom to be closed while the top half was left open, the stallion put his head out the opening. The lips of the two animals met in short feverish tremors: fleeting kisses between two creatures whose sole aim in coming together was to populate the world, and whose nostrils alone relayed this desire. Abruptly the stallion threw his head back and let out his great call, and the mare bowed slightly on her four legs, her throat gurgling tender sounds. This was the signal. Everything was set for the main act. Having taken care to turn the mare around, my father opened the door. With a smile of wonderment the men watched the stallion plunge into the land of his desire, and with such force that he seemed bent on reaching the very heart of his function and purpose. And yet a second time! For a few moments the men were lost in dreams of the beauty of these wondrous things found in "nature unspoiled".

Jos-la-Fiole was pleased to see that the job had been done with such promising vigour. He brought out his bottle and emptied it down to the last drop. His mare was "full" and so was he. They helped him harness up his "blonde", all panting and weakened by the amorous exploits she had just gone through. Pleased to see her satisfied, Jos gave her a few good slaps on the flanks and called her a whore, but she wouldn't budge, though she usually would flatten her ears back and kick whenever anyone laid a hand on her. (When the flesh is sated, bad temper melts away.)

Our friend would happily have spent another hour chatting, thanking my father, or praising the ardour of his stallion, but there was work to be done. He was helped up onto his cart, for he was too drunk to get up by himself.

"So long. Be seein' ya. And thanks again!"

He had no choice but to leave and laid his whip to the mare's rump. He had sat himself down in front of the load, just at the height of the rail, shaky but proud. What a day, after all, it had been! His mare already had a foal in her belly, he had some fine seed, not much but good stuff, eh? It had slipped through their fingers and was a lovely yellow colour—yellow like those little birds he had seen at the fair. That's what really counted: for the first time they had all gathered around his sack of seed and had marvelled.

He passed close to the house, lost in his dreams, his head filled with future fields of hay. Great seas of clover, red and white seas through which, even in winter, white hares leaped joyfully, pursued by love and intoxicated by the wind. And he, Jos-la-Fiole, rode through these seas perched atop a great twenty-foot threshing machine pulled by four white horses. They walked with their heads held high while the wind blew through the tree trunks in the nearby forest, creating a tremendous sound of music that roused up all the dormant joy in God's plants and creatures.

He had reached the part about the music in the tree trunks when he started down the hill. (There was a hill just behind my father's house with a right-angled curve at the bottom.) Since the music was very loud, and the white horses had captured his whole attention, he forgot that he was starting down the hill and didn't see that his real mare, weakened by her love play, was letting herself be pushed by the load instead of bracing her rump against the crupper. To top it off, just as our friend began to gather speed Monsieur le Curé headed into the curve from the opposite direction at the wheel of his splendid new car. (Perhaps it was the car of spiritual life.) Quite naturally, Jos saw nothing. It took a loud honk of the horn to bring him back to earth. However, numbed by alcohol he only had time to get entangled in his brake rope and the reins. The mare and the cart made a triumphant entry into Monsieur le Curé's car, which he had scarcely had time to stop. The impact threw Jos-la-Fiole from the top of the load onto the road. The priest managed to get out of his car, which was barely recognizable, and went over to Jos who was stretched out on the ground. He heard the dying man murmur:

"Why, it's you, Monsieur le Curé! You've had an accident with your new car"

Jos received absolution immediately and died without further delay. A fractured skull and several broken limbs: just when he was feeling truly happy.

Jean-Jules Richard

The 48 Hour Pass

Jean-Jules Richard is author of *Neuf jours de haine*, one of French-Canada's best war novels and a book, like Colin McDougall's *Execution*, that deserves to be much better known. Richard is self-schooled and works as a free-lance writer and journalist. He has published several novels dealing in a naturalistic style with the lives of asbestos miners, of a hobo during the Depression, of Montreal stevedores and drug-pushers. Most recently he has written a reconstruction of the life of Louis Riel, *Louis Riel, Exovide* (1972). The story included here is earlier work, taken from a collection entitled *Ville rouge* published in 1949.

Gilbert Drolet, the translator, who served with the Vingt-Deux's during the Korean War is now teaching English at Collège Militaire Royal at St. Jean, Quebec. He wrote his doctoral thesis on French- and English-Canadian war novels and is preparing a translation of Richard's *Neuf jours de haine*.

The 48 Hour Pass

The dark
street trills.
The cross-roads
squawk. Out of café doors
troops spill onto the sidewalks.
Soldiers' women too. Exuberance,
tumult, laughter and song. Cursing in English, French and Walloon. Invitations, propositions. The sweet life.

The boys are in town for two days.

"Let's go in here."

In they go.

Marius has had three cognacs. Percy has had three too. Because
they rush him, Franz makes a face as he swallows his third. On stage,
the performers give it all they've got. The house is packed. Women,
soldiers, civilians. The comedians joke in half-French, quarter-Eng-
lish and quarter-Walloon. All the spectators must be satisfied.
Marius is convulsed with laughter at Percy's bewilderment. And
Franz splits his sides just watching Marius.

Out they go. Next door a glass of Pernod.

Out again. Next door an absinthe.

They move on to the next door. Marius has stacks of francs. The
waiter takes what he wants. So much money and so little time to
spend it. Let's not complicate matters. Marius has already made this
clear. He wants to spend it on women. Percy hesitates. Franz laughs
like Marius. Let's go. Let's find some.

From club to club. Here there's dancing. That's luck! And women
to dance with, too.

In no time, they have made three conquests. Marius takes up with

a chubby dark girl called Loui-i-se. Percy speaks Walloon to a tall skinny woman named Greta, as assured as a stuffed goose. Franz is dancing with Jeannette.

Louise shakes her heavy head of hair, combed down to shoulder length. Straight, fuzzy, black hair. She chatters constantly with a little of that curtness characteristic of the Belgian accent. She is bursting with life, good humour, laughter and spontaneity. Marius is paired off with his weight in gold.

Greta puts on the distinguished air of a museum piece. Percy thinks she must have remote Puritan origins. A little English, a little Walloon, a little French. He is consumed by the warmth of her secrets. The motions of her hands explain nothing, nor do her shoulders.

Franz comes back with Jeannette. She jabbers a little German. He does too. It sounds like Polish, the language of his parents. But without the red wine, there would be nothing doing.

Then Marius becomes the official interpreter. Tell her this; tell him that. Answer this; answer that. This and that become confusing. They ask for cognac: a German brand. It tastes like lighter fluid and costs 75 francs. One, two, six, 300 francs. A little beer: German, to wash down the cognac.

Louise chatters noisily. She is a conscientious woman. She understands her role and plays it to the hilt. Like last night. . . .

"Loui-i-se, please don't talk about the soldiers you met last night," protests Greta.

This makes Marius laugh. Franz echoes him. Percy is puzzled.

"Go ahead," Marius insists. "Tell us about the soldiers you met last night."

Greta's bosom strains her bodice. Jeannette stares at Franz, who glances at Marius for the signal to laugh. Percy wants to dance. The orchestra grinds out a slightly outdated continental tune. As the couple leaves, Louise speaks of last night's soldiers, a little less of those from the night before, a little more of the ones three nights ago. It all dates back to the beginning of the Liberation.

Before that, there were Germans. Some were handsome, so handsome. Marius makes some caustic comments. Laughing, Jeannette and Franz leave the table. The waitress comes to ask them to settle up the last round. If Marius remembers rightly, Percy has already paid.

"But no! It hasn't been paid," says Louise, winking at the waitress.

"If it's money you want," says Marius, "help yourself."

Already 2200 hours. There's still time. Curfew is at 2330. Let's dance. Let's have fun. Life is so warm here. So different from the front where there is laughter too, but not so easy. Ah, yes! the front. Louise asks a few questions. But soon she is joking again.

"You've come here to have fun, right? To forget. You must forget. And if I want to invite you in for the night, I'll have to brighten you up, to keep you out of the dumps. Just imagine, last night I had three soldiers in my bed."

"And tonight?"

Tonight.

They are in Louise's apartment. Franz, Greta and Percy, sitting on a couch, leaning back against a wall. Two British soldiers and a Polish N.C.O. are lined up on another couch. Marius looks at them mischievously. Louise met them at the café exit. She insisted. They came.

But all of them, on the two couches and Marius in the arm-chair, are looking at Louise. She has climbed up on the table in the middle of the room.

She is dancing the hula.

Her legs. Her pounding feet. Her arms forming sensuous figures in the air. Her hands buried in emptiness as though it were solid. Her fingers, their skill. Her almost fuzzy hair. But her face, taut with the desire to please and amuse, her face provokes laughter only when Louise allows it. When she wants to suggest passion, her eyes sparkle with passion. Her mouth begs when she wants to arouse desire.

And Marius would find all this wonderful but his thoughts are focused on the outcome of the evening. The British, the Pole. And Jeannette hits the wrong keys on the piano.

Louise makes them all laugh. Then she holds them in a sort of a trance leading up to the climax. When Greta cries out:

"Loui-i-se, Jeannette."

Jeannette looks first. Louise is too absorbed in her act. Jeannette looks where the others are looking. Towards the front door.

There is a man there. He stands like a post, his head raised towards Louise. She is annoyed that the music has stopped. Her glance towards the piano makes her turn around. She jumps down from the table and runs to throw herself into the newcomer's arms.

"My husband, my husband," she shouts.

She lets them all know that her husband has returned. Here he is.

The Germans had conscripted him for war factory work. He has been gone for two years.

"Tell us about it, tell us," she says.

He doesn't feel like talking. He doesn't know what to do with his arms. Should he caress this naked woman or beat her? His fatigue seeps through his clothing. His flesh looks bloodless. He is exhausted. There is no need to speak. His looks convey their own meaning: *Go on. Get out.* Even Jeannette, who is only interested in Franz.

Complications increase. Greta shares the room with Louise, each to a bed. Jeannette stays on the sofa. It is after curfew. The soldiers can't leave. The two Englishmen maintain their composure. With his handkerchief, the Pole mops the sweat in the hollow of his neck.

Louise is still questioning her husband. She becomes more and more affectionate. Greta's complexion yellows like margarine. Marius nods to Percy and starts to speak with the husband. The husband speaks some French. Then the Pole speaks to him in German. Franz puts in a word; Greta half a word.

"Go and put some clothes on," Greta tells Louise.

She goes. The night is lost for Marius. At least the night of love. From here, he can see his bed at the Canadian hotel, empty and so inviting.

Well then, shall we go? The Englishmen are ready. The Pole seems to misunderstand. He has understood nothing from the start. Greta lets Percy get up. Jeannette pushes Franz back and holds him there. He will stay behind.

Life becomes as complicated as a chess game for Louise. After all, this husband must be properly welcomed. Jeannette takes pity on her. Poor Louise, this spells disaster for her life of wartime sacrifices. No. She decides simply to change her perspective. The husband must need affection every bit as much as three soldiers do.

Out into the street. At a corner, a patrol stops them, at rifle-point. Explanations are endless. They are escorted to their hotels. The Pole too. He still understands nothing.

A white bed, fresh sheets. After life at the front, how good it is to sleep, naked, until noon.

Already Percy is on the move. He knocks at Marius' door. Let's get going, let's have fun. Half the pass has already slipped by. Allied grub, in the dining-room, satisfies them for once. They'll have to shoot the cook when they get back to the front.

Then the excitement of the city. The townspeople smile at them. To some extent soldiers are public property. They can sense it. Women know it. The round of movie houses, pool halls, cafés, pubs, music halls, and everywhere they sense it and the women know it.

They stop at a photographer's. Percy and Marius face the camera, their arms around each other's shoulders. Unfortunately, Franz is not there. Then individual pictures are taken. Marius uses his battle smile, slightly mocking. Percy chides him. He assumes a gentle look for his mother.

Then a tour of the clubs on the side-streets. The intimate kind. It takes money, sweat and love. Marius disappears. When he returns, Percy is gone. After a quarter-hour, they meet again. Gratified, they rub their stomachs. After months of frustration, their bodies, finally fed, radiate well-being.

At supper, they find Franz. What a night! What a day! In the morning Jeannette was a mess. She had to go to the hairdresser's: 400 francs, a mere nothing. Then the wine drunk at the house yesterday, which no one had paid for: 400 francs, a trifle. And then the room, even if it was the living-room: 400 francs, nothing at all. And the husband who had come back, he needed so many things. A suit. Shoes. A hat. Several times 400 francs. Here they are. Think nothing of it.

Marius' derision is worth nothing. Franz is cleaned out. He needs money: 400 francs each, fellows. It's nothing.

They are invited to a party. At the same café? Of course not! They want a change, something new. They have to go back; Franz insists. Louise promised to be there at her best in a generous spirit.

Louise dancing at the cabaret tonight. What about her husband?

European morals, old boy. . . .

The orchestra twangs. Percy and Greta are dancing. Jeannette wears herself out smothering Franz and he is tired of being coddled. Louise makes small talk with Marius. Her home problems. She'd rather not dance. Marius would rather laugh. He listens and she's as zestful as ever. But he also pays for the drinks. Poor Franz is wiped out and Louise has to see the hairdresser tomorrow.

"Four hundred francs, it's nothing," Marius exclaims.

The inference surprises her, but it makes her laugh. Percy must also be fleeced. What possible use will all that money be at the front? Besides, you can never tell what might happen.

Wine. Bad cognac. German beer. Better get out. At the house they'll buy some good wine.

"Four hundred francs," Franz laughingly blurts out, anticipating Marius. Percy is still as shy as ever. All the better for him. Greta prefers him that way. They would be a beautiful couple to have stuffed.

The last drink must be paid.

"Four hundred francs, it's nothing," sneers Marius.

"Four hundred and twenty francs," the waitress stresses. And that doesn't include the tip.

She never understood how the settling of a bill could cause so much laughter.

Louise's apartment. Franz, Greta, Percy, like last night. On the other sofa, two Belgian resistance fighters. Louise dragged them along on the way from the club.

They all watch Louise. She has climbed onto the large table. Her feet—her hands—her hair. Her expression prompts laughter, when she allows it.

Marius would find this pleasant. But he is uneasy. How will it all end? They should leave. The town patrol. To get caught twice in a row. Jeannette hits flats instead of sharps on the piano. The Belgian partisans are ecstatic watching the dance.

The door. No one at the door.

The husband. No husband.

The climax.

Louise is proud of the effect. The onlookers cheer. Breathless Louise drags Marius to the sofa where the two Belgians are sitting. She kisses and hugs them in turn. The two excited Belgians laugh. Marius laughs too. Then she announces:

"Let's go to bed."

"And your husband?" asks Marius.

"Him! He won't bother me tonight," she says.

He wanted to stop her from following her calling. Her vocation was to comfort the fighting men, who would die tomorrow. Yes, it was a life of sacrifice. He wanted all this to stop. So she had him arrested as a collaborator.

"That'll teach him," she says. "Now, come on. Come on, all of you. Well, what are you waiting for? Aren't you coming?"

Gilles Vigneault

The Bus Driver
The Buyer
The Wall

Gilles Vigneault was born in 1928 in the North Shore village of Natashquan that he has made famous in his songs. Everyone knows him as a poet and the most popular Quebec chansonnier of his generation. But few people are aware that his gifts for creating character and situation in his songs have also been doubled in prose. He has published two volumes of the kind of short-short story that is presented here. The first has been translated as *Tales on Tiptoe* by Paul Allard (Press Porcépic, 1972). The second collection, *Contes du coin de l'oeil* (1966) from which these stories are taken, has not been translated yet. The challenge is to capture the nervousness of Vigneault's rhythm, the simplicity and suggestiveness of his words, and the twinkle of humour that offsets the basic sadness of these brief stories.

Jacqueline de Puthod is a Parisienne who usually translates from English to French. She is at present working on a French rendering of Alice Munro's *Dance of The Happy Shades*. This is her first translation in the reverse direction.

The Bus Driver

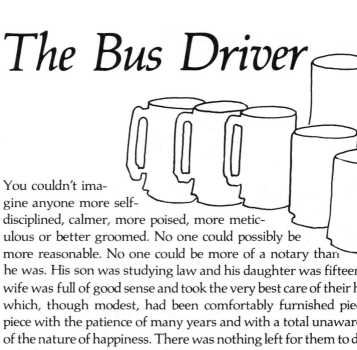

You couldn't imagine anyone more self-disciplined, calmer, more poised, more meticulous or better groomed. No one could possibly be more reasonable. No one could be more of a notary than he was. His son was studying law and his daughter was fifteen. His wife was full of good sense and took the very best care of their house which, though modest, had been comfortably furnished piece by piece with the patience of many years and with a total unawareness of the nature of happiness. There was nothing left for them to do but to be happy. Monsieur Léon Laurent was not. This realization came to him one winter evening as he was coming home at four o'clock, the "wee hour" as he used to call it. The February day had been mild and greyish outside, long and tedious inside the office, and he had been badgered all afternoon by an undefined feeling that it would have been too easy to call boredom. At the second to last traffic light before his street, he had already projected into his home that vague image of oneself that one keeps hovering at the surface of the daily routine, when he realized as only a notary can realize, just how little everything that made up his life seemed to interest him any more. Then a bizarre idea emerged that was going to carry him beyond his familiar world out into the unknown. When he had put his car into the garage, instead of coming in as he did every evening and settling down with his ritual paper after kissing his wife on the forehead and his daughter on both cheeks (he did think of this, nevertheless, as he walked), he decided to walk out into the city.

He soon found himself in the lower part of town where, he remembered, a rather casual client of his used to live, one who had given him a cheque that bounced two years previously.

He noticed with astonishment that these streets teemed with a type of life that seemed infinitely more real than that of his own street. Then he took a bus home.

"I just went for a little walk. Sitting down all day I'm getting stiff in the joints."

But it didn't seem to have disturbed the usual routine at home as he had feared. He discovered that he was his own master and that he had the right to take whatever walks he pleased.

He let two days go by, however, before changing worlds again. This time (he was getting more and more aware of his own solitude and the boredom of his life), he entered a restaurant.

"A coffee."

A taxi driver (no, a bus driver) was talking to a worker behind him.

"I met him at the tavern."

"Not the tavern right next door here?"

"Yeah, that's the one."

"Well, speak of the devil! He's one of my best friends. It's a pretty small world, eh?"

He didn't hear the rest, paid, and went out.

In front of the sign LA TAVERNE DES BONS AMIS he told himself: "Next time."

It happened the following day and it was unforgettable.

The tavern was full. People looked up from at least two tables. But he had the impression that the whole world had stopped drinking to watch the notary take a glass of beer. None the less, it seemed that in this world, totally foreign to him as it was, things happened by themselves. So, after the third time, he left a reasonable tip, paid a round to his table, and talked to everyone like a regular.

"What about you, Léon? What kinda job d'you have?"

"Me. . . I'm a driver."

"A driver?"

"Yes, a bus driver."

It came to him quite naturally.

"Come on up to my place. You don't know anybody. That'll be somewheres to go. A man's got to have friends. Come and have supper."

That is how this strange existence started for the notary who was always an hour late coming home.

The office had become a joy. And the modest but comfortable home a routine acquired through many patient years. But the secret part of the game invites you to invent as you go along. He had actually become part of a universe in which he lived as a perpetual guest.

He kept his slippers there, and his favourite habits. The pipes he smoked there were exhilarating, the most ordinary stew became a dish fit for a king, and the beer was always rich and strong. Sometimes he would get back around midnight into his ordinary notary's skin with his head still aglow with mysterious flares.

In the course of three months there had been a few cleverly turned questions, some inspired explanations, suspicions and a bit of teasing, but no serious trouble.

It's at the source of every happiness that one should expect to find its death, too.

It was a May-like day outside and they had gone for a pipe into the small backyard where Henri's children would soon be burning leaves.

"Say, Léon, my brother Arsène, the one I told you about who had three woodlots and some houses up at St. Etienne, he's dead."

Then after a while:

"He was the oldest, and as I'm the youngest he's leaving me his houses and a piece of land. Except they say his will wasn't proper and his brother-in-law wants to make trouble. Don't know what to do."

"Go and see a notary," the bus driver said without batting an eye.

"Don't know any. Them notaries it's like lawyers, the less you see of them the better off you are."

"Go and see a good notary. Wait a minute, when my father died, I remember...."

The name and address of a colleague, someone sure, efficient, very competent.

But the next day at eleven o'clock Monsieur Laurent heard as in a dream, when all movements are accelerated and the issue is brought to a head in a flash, the voice of his secretary saying in her usual polite way: "There's a Monsieur Henri Langer here, sir. He would like to see you right away."

The colleague was away. He should have known better. A finger flicks the bottom card and the whole card house suddenly collapses. It would never be the same after this.

"Show him in."

Three months of real life. Henri came in.

"But . . . it's Lé. . . . You are Monsieur Léon."

"Yes, Henri. I'm a notary. Sit down. Don't be scared. I'm going to fix things up for you. You'll see. You're not too mad at me are you?"

No, Henri didn't seem to mind. He even seemed quite happy to

know so well someone so important. And he would get used to calling him Léon. And. . .

But that evening Léon came home at four.

"Winter's really over."

"Oh, it's you?"

"Yes. It's me."

The Buyer

One winter day,
upon returning from
his trapper's cabin, my father announced
happily that he had met the fur buyer. They
had stopped their dog sleds to greet each other.
"I'll drop over to see you," the buyer said. "I've got
two or three squirrel tails to show you," my father had answered,
laughing.

The buyer came. He had a foreign name which I have forgotten.
He sat down, accepted a drink and talked with my father about the
snow, about the March storms,and about the wood that had been
cut that winter. About the furs, not a word. They eyed one another.
Under cover of their conversation I had crept into the room, the
living room in our home, where the furs were piled up nearly as high
as me (I was six then). The red foxes and the silver ones, the mixed,
the white and black and those that were all grey; the brown and black
minks, the most beautiful of all; the long otters, so soft to the touch,
and the lynxes, those big cats that behave like tigers and about which
every trapper has a terrible story to tell when he comes back from his
cabin. Then, on the top of the pile, covering the muskrats, were the
weasels that seemed so white, and sometimes whiter still when there
was a spot as black as jet against their snowy fur, and also the squirrels. A trapper is not a sportsman and if sometimes my father took
weasels and squirrels, it was because they sold well. The two men
were behind me, measuring each other, trying to outguess each
other, each keeping an eye on the impressive pile of furs.

The buyer spoke first. "Can I have a look?"

Without waiting for an answer that wasn't going to come, he
reached for the pelts, started shaking them, held them up to the light,
stroked them and blew on the fur. It went on and on for over an
hour. From time to time he would make a comment, show appre-

ciation, or give a disapproving "Huh" without ever raising an echo. I kept a close watch on my father's silence. I could feel him being hunted. The trap laid before him was a word that shouldn't have been said, or should have. It was hard to say which.

When he was through, the buyer declared without raising an eyebrow, as if talking to the stack of pelts: "Not worth much. Pity, too. Would have been good fur. This year it's beaver. Don't have any beaver, do you?"

My father said nothing. But his silence was like an icy wind blowing over the plains at dusk carrying tomorrow's snow. His silence was as hard as the ice covering the lakes on the other side of Blue Mountain.

The buyer added, as if talking to himself, quite determined not to change his mind and ready to shake the dust from off his feet: "Could give you a hundred bucks for the lot, but I wonder what I'd do with them."

Then my father, who is the most hospitable man I know, asked him politely to get out. The other did, in a hurry, without even daring to offer an excuse. He was in such haste to be elsewhere.

There was not another buyer the whole winter long and every evening my father would go into the room and say to himself: "What insults me most is to have killed all those poor animals for nothing."

In the spring he sold the lot to a merchant who dealt in something else. Two hundred and fifty dollars. It was nothing. As for me, I had got quite used to all those beasts in "the parlour" and when I discovered, coming back from school one lovely April afternoon, that the fur corner was completely empty, I started to cry and declared to everyone that it was the buyer who had come back to steal them and I would kill him. No one told me otherwise. And one day I will.

The Wall

A former mason,
sentenced to twenty
years' hard labour, was repairing
with surprising care the exterior wall
of his prison. He was of course closely guarded, and
although the work was compulsory and under scrupulous surveill-
ance, the taste for perfection he exhibited at it was a source of
amazement to passers-by and even to his two guards. Someone expressed his surprise and the former mason, without lifting his eyes
from his work, replied as if he had expected the question all along:
"What pleasure would there be in escaping from a prison that was
poorly built?"

Then, before the anxious prison guards who had become more
watchful than ever, he went on as though talking to himself: "When
you've put your own hand to the making of a wall, it tells you more
about human freedom than all the philosophers put together."

This saying spread far and wide until it reached the ears of a monk.
The monk came to visit the mason. They talked together at length.
And the mason, without disturbing a soul, left the prison by the main
gate wearing a habit and a rope belt.

The prison director, a subtle man though he didn't show it, recently asked a professional burglar to repair a window sash. The
work was so well done that one feels something is bound to happen,
despite the formal order issued that day forbidding anyone to speak
to a prisoner at work.

Claire Martin

Follow Me
Springtime

Claire Martin came late to the profession of letters. Her first book, from which these two selections are taken, was a collection of short stories, *Avec ou sans amour*, published in 1959 when she was forty-five. Since then she has written three novels and an outstanding autobiography, *In an Iron Glove* (1966). Recently she has been writing for the stage and translating narratives of Eskimo life. On the strength of this accomplishment she has become one of the foremost writers and one of the most eloquent spokesmen for her sex in Quebec.

Claire Martin doesn't just look at people; her direct brown eyes pinpoint and scrutinize their object. A gleam in them denotes the pinch of malicious humour that will flavour her observation. Their unwavering gaze warns that she is going to pursue her subject with a kind of predatory attention.

"To be a child or a woman is always, like being destitute or coloured, a hazardous situation," she writes in her preface to *In an Iron Glove*. In the following stories she picks her way with feline dexterity through two such hazardous situations.

Philip Stratford translated the two volumes of Claire Martin's memoirs, *Dans un gant de fer* and *La Joue droite*, for The Ryerson Press in 1968. He has also translated *Convergences* by Jean Le Moyne and has published a critical study of Marie-Claire Blais (Forum House, 1970).

Follow Me

He's still there, behind
me. Among all the other
noises in the street my ear
picks out the sound of his feet. It's
perfectly idiotic, of course. I think I must be a little mad. What's so
important about being followed by a man? It's happened a hundred
times before. But there it is; perhaps today is the last time

Have you even had a good look at my face, you behind me, following so confidently after my well-tailored dress, my well-corseted
figure and my ash-blonde hair—my hairdresser's special triumph?
Yes, you've seen it. But this big hat with its pink lining is a trick. It's
lucky I've come straight from the beauty salon. Lucky? What do I
mean? I *am* a little mad, just as I was saying.

You're walking quickly, little man. I'm already beginning to feel
slightly tired. The thing is, you see, I mustn't let you pass me. You'd
think I was giving in. And right then I'd have to set you straight.
You'd cross over to the other side of the street. Let me go on being
followed a bit longer. Don't walk so fast, little man.

The first time, I was just about your age. He was older, about my
age now. I was peeved. At seventeen one is more sensitive to the
insult of it than the flattery. And I was ashamed because a young
woman who is being followed by an older man always thinks that he
thinks she can be bought. I tried to look as much like a well-bred
young lady as I could. And he followed me all the more avidly. Finally,
I went into a church and hid in the confessional. When he couldn't
find me he made a broad genuflexion and dropped a coin in the poor
box under the statue of Saint Anthony. He was a humorist.

Look out now, not so close! Keep your distance, young man. And
whatever you do, don't speak to me. At that age they're shy. And like
all shy people they tend to be impudent. Don't speak. You're following me, that's fine. But follow like a gentleman. Don't turn out to

be one of those who can't even guess whether a woman will or won't. You can tell that, even from behind.

I really don't see what pleasure you take in this silly sport. When I was young I used to imagine that a man had to be sex-starved to practise it. I scorned men who were incapable of making a normal conquest. Still do, I must admit. It was only much later I understood that you don't have to be starved to prowl. So why do it?

There are, of course, men who prefer tarts. Theirs is a simple case. But the ones who follow us? Is it the pleasure of getting on a woman's nerves, seeing her stumble, chasing her from one sidewalk to the other, waiting at the door of the shop where she's taken refuge and, when she comes out, having a long cool look at her offended face—for she keeps her eyes down of course. Are they that subtle?

And then there are those who just fancy a pretty pair of legs. Pursuit puts them in the front row centre. Now that was really a smart thing to do, wasn't it? Whether my seam is straight or not, this wasn't the time to touch it. Really smart. Naturally, he comes closer. What a fool I'm being. I'm beginning to have enough.

Wasn't it funny that time my husband followed me for a quarter of an hour without recognizing me? I was wearing a completely new outfit from head to toe, right down to those thick shoes in fashion that spring that changed your height and the way you walked. I recognized him by his cough. I think I could pick it out, one in ten thousand, blindfold. Followers are great coughers. I stole a glance in my pocket mirror at his unknown face. How stunned he was when I turned around! And the lovely compact he gave me the next day!

Then there are those who can never understand that women whom convention has decreed to call "respectable" sometimes have to cross through shady districts. Or others who for other reasons simply can't get their eyes lined up behind their eye-holes. Like that poor devil, abysmally drunk, who asked me between hiccups "Well, are you or ain't you?" and lifted his hat and said, "Thank you," most politely when I replied, "No, I am not."

And what about you? What are you thinking? What are you hoping? Aren't you getting a little tired of it all? You're pretty patient for your age. It's rare. And yet you've got lots of time ahead of you. All that time, while I . . . . If I were really mad I'd stop in front of that display of little blue hats. Maybe the things you'd say wouldn't be all that disappointing. What would you offer me? A cup of coffee? In there? It looks nice. And not too bright. And after that? Your student's room? You'd hand me a cigarette in fingers that were slightly chapped and trembling. And maybe not very clean either. I can see your face when I'd take off my gloves and you'd see my rings. And my pink silk underwear with the open lace embroidery. Yes—rings and embroidered lingerie aren't enough to make a person forget the knotted veins in the backs of hands and the heavy creases a girdle leaves.

And what about you? Would your youth be enough to make me forget your ignorance, your clumsiness, your foolish talk? Would it make me forget the image you have of me?

Give it up, little man. Can't you see I'm tired and that I have to straighten my back every ten steps or so? You're walking too fast. Can't you see my ankles are swollen from having been pursued so long? You've given me an hour of your life. If you knew how grateful I am, you'd be amazed. I didn't see your face for long, but I won't forget it.

What am I doing now? Why, going into this bra and corset shop. It's an old ruse. Not one of them dares follow you here. Good-bye, little man—and thanks.

Springtime

The neighbours laughed when Miss Amelia went by. The women would shrug their shoulders, which set their bountiful breasts bouncing under their flowered housecoats. The children, repeating what they had heard their parents say, would shout after her, "Crazy old maid! Crazy old maid!"

Miss Amelia wouldn't even deign to lift an eyelid. Stiffly, in her black dress, she would pass on by.

Poor Amelia. It's true she was still a maid, but she wasn't old. Thirty-five, thirty-eight maybe. In the prime of life. And not ugly either. But her face was always ravaged by rage.

From the back she was enticing enough to be followed frequently. By men who were strangers to the neighbourhood, it should be noted. Anger, her daily bread, kept her as thin as a garter snake, gave a spring to her step, and an extraordinary toss to her head. Compared to the old housefraus on the block, she made you think of an unbroken mare in a field of fat cows.

The follower, being attracted to nervous women, would trot along behind. Drawing abreast, he would stop dumbfounded, then hurry right on by. There wasn't a single one who ever thought of anything but escape, followed by the laughter of the natives.

She had a look like a bull whip, did Miss Amelia. You really had to be a stranger not to know its devastating effects.

There was only one person, the lady who lived on the third floor left, who tried to be kind to her. It wasn't easy, yet she didn't give up trying. She was the persevering sort, a woman who followed her notions right through to the end.

Since she was going through her third husband, Miss Amelia's case seemed triply pathetic to her. "The poor thing," she would sigh. "Just put yourself in her shoes. Have you seen those red hot coals in her eyes? She's burning up, she is! It's all very well to say, better marry than burn. But Saint Paul doesn't say what to do when you're only a woman and no husband comes forward."

With that she would pull a little pout for the misogynist saint and then dissolve in pretty smiles and confusion. In her case, husbands flocked forward like indigents to a soup kitchen.

It was mainly her brother Charles, lately come to the neighbourhood, whom the wife from the third floor left chose as confidant for her compassion. Charles was fortyish, a shoemaker, and a good-looking man. And like his sister he had a heart that was tender and understanding.

The day he saw the old maid come into his shop with her offended face, he couldn't resist the sudden urge to be a little bit nice to her, just to see. A compliment is quickly made, doesn't cost anything, and can't lead very far. As he was a shoemaker, he looked at her foot, quickly saw that it was slender and nicely arched, and told her as much.

Now it so happened that Miss Amelia had always been quite proud of her feet. Perhaps she had always been waiting for someone to say something nice about them. Perhaps that was all she held against the human race, their ignorance of the fact that her feet existed. Her expression softened. She inclined her head gently and gave a little laugh as fresh as a schoolgirl's upon leaving the convent at the end of term.

Down she sat, took off her shoe, and put her foot up on the low stool. Charles felt impelled to rush forward, he knew he should have, but he stood there like a simpleton. The sparkle of her teeth, the curve of her foot, the caress of her laugh, had gone straight to his heart, and he was filled with a kind of fearful joy.

When the worst of his emotion had passed, he got out his finest shoes, shoes that were supple and soft as a girl's cheek. He could see how his trembling hands gave him away, but he didn't care. If a man doesn't speak, you can't slap him for trembling, can you? And apart from a slap he was ready for anything.

Courage! The moment had come. He seized her foot with just the right degree of warmth and slipped it into the shoe. "It fits like a glove! And you notice I didn't even ask your size." It was true. This happy stroke seemed to lend the whole affair a flavour of predestination that was troublesome indeed.

He stayed there holding the narrow foot closely in his hand. She felt the burn through the leather. Silently she savoured this unknown happiness, thinking all the while that the other foot was cold too. He let her have the shoes at cost. For him she was already almost the boss. At cost price. And he blushed when he took the money.

Miss Amelia's romance left the neighbourhood stunned and bewildered. The news dominated the conversations of the local gossips. Doors and windows filled with heads as she passed by.

That the old maid was loved and in love was already grist to their mill, but even more astounding was her new physical appearance. Each day that went by put a little more velvet in her look, a little more satin to her skin, and a sort of abandon in the roll of her hips. Now her ankles betrayed her and she would stumble when she walked out under Charles' admiring gaze. Her knees buckled under the miracle.

The grocer's wife, who had been chosen by her husband because she was solidly built and could stay on her feet behind the counter twelve hours at a stretch without grumbling, and who had accepted because the grocery business is the most serious of all commercial enterprises, followed this metamorphosis with an astonished eye and sighed all day long.

Charles' sister came close to believing that there must be a strain of sorcery in the family. She talked to her third husband at great length about it. So much so that the poor man began to get shivers down his spine whenever she looked at him, as she often did now with a mildly haggard expression as if seeing through him. He couldn't help feeling that the spell hadn't been exhausted yet and that it was a fourth chance at happiness his wife was watching as it advanced through the promise-laden fog of the future.

When Amelia and Charles announced their marriage, the neighbourhood breathed a sigh of relief. At last things were going to return to normal. Everyone had managed to survive the courtship, but it would be nice to get back to preoccupations a little less torrid. By the wedding day, interest was already on the wane. The lovers were turning out just like everyone else.

A month hadn't passed before a little of the old Miss Amelia—just a trifle—began to show through. At first just a slight tensing of the nostrils. A few weeks later and it had spread to her mouth. After six months she had got back the two furrows between her eyebrows.

Nobody noticed because nobody was particularly interested any more. From time to time they would size up the state of her belly, but when that showed no signs of change they thought about something else.

It wasn't till months later that two old cronies, whiling away their time pinching lettuce heads, were struck by a sense of *déjà vu* when Miss Amelia walked by. She had completely recovered her prancing gait, her furious face, and her whiplash look.

The two old women burst out laughing and began slapping their thighs. After all, nobody expected that dreamy mood to last a lifetime, did they?

Poor Amelia, would she ever remember anything about that spring, that gentle madness, that brief blossoming?

Michel Tremblay

The Hanged Man
Mister Blank
The Thimble

Michel Tremblay is the most promising young (b. 1944) dramatist in Quebec today. His first full-length play, *Les Belles-Soeurs*, a study of the envious frenzy that descends on a group of Montreal housewives when one of them wins a million supermarket trading stamps, was the hit of the 1968 season. Tremblay went on from there to adapt *Lysystrata* for the opening of the National Arts Centre and to write half a dozen other plays and adaptations (most recently *Hosanna* and a scenario, *Françoise Durocher, Waitress*), which have kept him in the theatre public's eye ever since.

But he has also written a science fiction fantasy, *La Cité dans l'oeuf* (1969), and a book of short stories, *Contes pour buveurs attardés* (1966), from which the following tales are taken. They are miniature nightmares which start in panic and build to catastrophe. The strangeness of Tremblay's invention and the tautness of his technique are quite remarkable.

Jay Bochner teaches English at l'Université de Montréal. He has written a book on Blaise Cendrars, reviews frequently for the Toronto *Globe and Mail*, and has translated prose and poetry for *Ellipse*.

The Hanged Man

In my
country when
someone kills his
neighbour, we hang
him. It's certainly
stupid, but that's what we do.
It's the law.

As for myself, I watch the hanged men. In the
prison where I work, when the man is dead we don't take him down
right away. Quite the contrary, we let him hang all night, and as
watchman I sit with him until sunrise.

I am not asked to cry, but I do it anyway.

I could tell that this man was not going to be an ordinary hanged
man. All the condemned men I had seen until then had been afraid,
but this one wasn't. He was not smiling, but still there was no fright
in his eyes. He studied the gallows coolly, whereas all the others
almost invariably became hysterical when they saw it. Certainly this
was not going to be an ordinary hanged man.

When the trap opened and the rope went taut with a sharp sound I
felt something move in my stomach.

The man did not flail about. All the ones I had seen before
thrashed and twisted, swung on the end of their rope bending their
knees; but this one didn't move.

He wasn't dead right off. You could hear him trying to breathe.
But he didn't move. Not the least movement. The hangman, the
prison director and myself, we looked at each other and scratched
our heads. It lasted some minutes and then, all of a sudden, the man
gave a long howl that seemed to me the boundless laugh of a madman. The hangman said that was the end.

The man shuddered, his body seemed to lengthen a bit, and then, nothing.

As for me, I was sure he had laughed.

I was alone with the hanged man who had laughed. I couldn't keep from looking at him. He seemed to have become longer. And that hood I have always hated! The hood hides everything, but it also lets you guess everything. I never see the faces of the hanged, but I can guess what they look like, and that is more terrible by far, I think.

All the lights were out, except the little night-light above the door.

It was so dark, and I was afraid of the hanged man.

About two o'clock I dozed off in spite of myself. I was awakened, I don't know when, by a small noise that sounded like a long breath, or a sigh. Was that my own sigh? It must have been, since I was alone. I had probably sighed in my sleep and woken myself up.

Instinctively I turned to the hanged man. He had moved. He had turned ninety degrees and now faced in my direction. That wasn't the first time such a thing had happened, and I knew very well it was caused by the rope, but I couldn't keep from trembling anyhow. And that sigh! I couldn't be sure that it had come from me.

What a complete idiot, I said to myself, and I stood up to walk a bit. As soon as my back was turned to the hanged man I heard the sigh again. This time I knew for sure that it had not been me. I couldn't turn around. My legs grew weak and my throat went dry. I heard two or three more sighs, and these became breathing, at first uneven and then more regular. I was absolutely certain the body was breathing, and I felt all my strength drain away.

Finally I turned, shaking. The corpse was moving. He was swaying slowly, almost imperceptibly at the end of his rope. He was breathing louder and louder. I fell back as far as I could from him, to the farthest corner of the big room.

I will never forget the horrible scene that followed. The hanged man had been breathing for about five minutes when suddenly he began to laugh quietly. It was not an evil laugh, or even a cynical one, but merely the laughter of a fellow having a delightful time. Soon it grew in volume, and in no time the hanged man was convulsed with laughter. His sides were shaking, and he was swinging higher and higher, and laughing, laughing.

I was sitting on the floor, my arms clutching my stomach, and I was crying.

The corpse swung so high that his feet almost touched the ceiling. For a few moments of terror he swung higher. Suddenly the rope broke and I screamed. The man fell to the floor with a thud. His head came off and rolled right up to me. I jumped up and fled towards the door.

When the guard, the prison director and I returned to the room the body was still there, lying in a corner. But we couldn't find the dead man's head. We never found it.

Mister Blank

Mister Blank was dumbfounded. What kind of a game was this? Who had dared. . . . . In front of him, on the wooden wall that ran along Cedar Street, was a huge poster, and from the middle of this poster Mister Blank smiled back at himself. Above his photograph, in violent red lettering a foot high, was an incredible sentence that startled Mister Blank: *Vote Blank, candidate of the future!*

Mister Blank removed his glasses and wiped them nervously. He put them back on his nose and looked at the poster again.

He was frightened. He started to run, and jumped onto the first bus to come by. "Impossible, it's impossible," Mister Blank said to himself. "I was dreaming, I must have been! Me, a candidate?"

For weeks people had been talking about these elections. They would surely be the most important elections of the century. One thing was certain, the two major parties were going to fight it out to the death.

Mister Blank was trembling. He tried to read his paper, but he couldn't concentrate on the little black letters that seemed to swarm like crazed flies.

For weeks people had talked about these elections. "Come on, I must have been mistaken!" The most important elections of the century. Without a doubt the most important elections of the century. "It's a joke." The most important . . . . Suddenly he cried out. In the centre-fold of his paper was the biggest picture he had ever seen in a newspaper, right in the middle, spread over the whole page. There he was. There was Mister Blank, and he was smiling, at himself. *Vote Blank, candidate of the future!* He folded his paper and threw it out the window.

Directly across from him a little boy leaned over to his mother and said, "Mommy, look, the man in the poster!" Recognizing Mister

Blank, the little boy's mother jumped up and rushed at the poor man, who thought he would die of fear. "Mister Blank," exclaimed the lady as she seized his hands, "Mister Blank, our saviour!" She kissed Mister Blank's hands, and he seemed about to have a fit. "Come now, dear lady," he blurted out finally, "I am not your saviour." But the woman was already screaming as if she were quite mad, "Long live Mister Blank, our saviour!" All the people in the bus repeated together, "Long live Mister Blank. . . ."

At his neighbourhood drugstore Mister Blank bought a bottle of aspirin. "So, going into politics now, are you?" said the druggist. He wore a blue ribbon pinned to his lapel, with lettering in red. . . .

The super's wife stopped him. "Mister Blank," she said, "you wouldn't by any chance have an extra ticket for your big convention tonight, would you?" Mister Blank almost tripped back down the few steps he had just climbed. Convention? What convention? Come on now, there wasn't any convention! "Oh you are the secretive one! I should have known important things were going on in that head of yours. You can bet you sure surprised us, me and my husband."

That evening Mister Blank had no supper. If he had wanted to eat he would not have been able. The phone didn't stop ringing. His supporters wanted to know when he would get to the convention hall. Mister Blank thought he would go mad. He took the phone off the hook, put out the lights in his apartment, put on his pyjamas and went to bed.

The crowd demanded their saviour with great shouting in the street. They even threatened to break down his door if he didn't open it within ten minutes. Then the super's wife said a terrible thing that almost started a riot: "Mister Blank may be sick," she said to a journalist. Ten seconds later the crowd had knocked down his door and was triumphantly carrying off its saviour in his pyjamas. What an original outfit! It was a fine publicity stunt. A few men even went home to slip on their own pyjamas. Women in night-gowns went into the streets and followed the procession, intoning hymns of praise. Mister Blank was stunned and could not budge as he sat on the shoulders of the two most respected journalists in the country.

The convention was a smash. Mister Blank did not speak.

The new party, the people's party, Mister Blank's party burst upon the political scene like a bombshell. The old parties got only catcalls.

Slavery was abolished, thanks to Mister Blank. B-L-A-N-K. Blank!

Blank! Blank! Hurrah! No more tax hikes, Mister Blank would see to that. No more increases in the cost of living. Blank! Blank! Blank!

Only once did Mister Blank attempt to stand and say something. But the crowd cheered so much he was afraid of provoking them and sat down again.

They plied him with champagne, and in the end Mister Blank agreed he was a great hero. As a souvenir of this memorable evening, Mister Blank took home a huge pennant on which, in two-foot letters. . . .

The next day Mister Blank was elected Prime Minister.

The Thimble

If Bobby Stone had
known what was to happen that day,
he probably would never have got out
of bed. And . . . well, the catastrophe might
have been avoided.

Bobby Stone wasn't a bad fellow. He worked in an office, drank in moderation, went to mass every Sunday, and had a weakness for plump women. He was neither old nor young, though he wore a hat to cover an expanding bald spot.

Bobby Stone had not the slightest inkling that he was going to be the cause of the catastrophe.

"Now, now, my dear lady, please stop this silly game. People are looking at us!" He was right. A throng of loafers had gathered around them and some were beginning to eye Bobby Stone reproachfully, because this woman was weeping and wailing. "Sir, I beg of you," she cried, "take it! Take it! I give it to you. It's yours! " But Bobby Stone didn't want it; he didn't want to have anything to do with it. "What do you expect me to do with it?" he said. "And besides, it's a . . . thing that belongs to women." More and more people gathered on the sidewalk and Bobby Stone began to sweat. He took out his handkerchief to wipe his forehead, but he didn't remove his hat. *She's crazy. That's it, she's crazy. And all those people looking at us. But I don't want to have her thimble!*

A man emerged from the crowd and grabbed Bobby Stone by the collar. "So," he said, breathing a rotten smell into his face, "we make women cry in the middle of the street?" Bobby Stone was trembling. "But Mister, I don't know this woman! She wants to give me her thimble, and I don't want her thimble, I don't . . . . " Really, Bobby Stone had had enough. In an abrupt surge of courage—or was it cowardice?—he slammed his fist into the face of the man who was threatening him and took off, knocking over two or three people who tried to stop him.

As you might have expected, he worked very poorly that day. The columns of figures swayed on the page, and when he closed his eyes Bobby Stone saw the strange woman offering him the thimble. "It is yours."

The five o'clock bell rang. Bobby Stone slumped in his desk chair, his tie undone and one hand on his chest. *I never would have believed such a stupid incident . . . . Oh, no, that's too much, following me to my office!* But it was no vision this time; his eyes were wide open. She was sitting in the chair directly in front of him on the other side of his desk. "If you do not take it immediately," said the woman, "I will have to forbid you from taking it, and then you'll run after me to steal it from me. I'm telling you, you'll steal it from me." Bobby Stone, mad with fear, jumped up and ran towards the door. "Very well then," the woman cried out, "I forbid you to take my thimble!" Bobby Stone stopped short. Oh, what a fine thimble, such a fine beautiful thimble! Made out of plastic with tiny dimples in it. A fine thimble! He must have this thimble. Nothing else in the world existed outside of this pink and yellow thimble. He ran after the woman, who pretended to flee but was careful to lose ground all the while. . . .

Smack! And another! You bitch! So, you wanted to keep it all to yourself, did you? The thimble for you and nothing for me! This is for you. Some good kicks, you see, and the back of my hand, and a few with the knee. . . .

When he left the building his clothes were all mussed and there was some blood on his fingernails, but he had the thimble. It was his and no one—but no one, do you hear?—would ever be able to take it from him. He knew the secret of the thimble now. Before she died the woman had whispered, "In the thimble . . . in the thimble . . . I have locked the universe."

When he awoke the next morning Bobby Stone remembered nothing. He found a pink and yellow thimble on his night-table. What an ugly thimble! He threw it in the garbage. But before he left for the office Bobby Stone tore a loose button from his overcoat. He found some thread and a needle and thought of the thimble at the bottom of the garbage pail. He went and got it. And so as not to prick himself while he sewed on his coat button, Bobby Stone pushed his little finger into the little thimble. He squashed the entire universe.   *93 + The Thimble*

Jean Tétreau

The Great Disappearing Act

Jean Tétreau is a producer for Radio-Canada. He has written two volumes of short stories, *La Volupté de l'amour et de la mort* (1968), from which "The Great Disappearing Act" is taken, and *Treize histoires en noir et blanc* (1970), as well as a novel and several volumes of essays. His stories generally have international settings which reflect the years when the author was director of the CBC's information services in Paris.

This story shows him at his best, beginning strong, building confidently to stronger and stronger climaxes, and finishing off with a Raoul Dahl-like ending. There is a great deal of the conjurer in Tétreau's art. His wit and his shrewd sense of timing and psychology lead us to abandon ourselves to the enjoyment of an increasingly fantastic performance. Like Robertson Davies, he also knows the appeal of unadulterated magic.

Daniel Slote teaches in the translation programme at l'Université de Montréal. For many years he taught English literature at l'Institut Catholique in Paris, has published a translation of Rimbaud's *Illuminations,* and a book of his own poetry, *Poems in Miniature* (1972).

The Great Disappearing Act

Boudini's fame
was such that
the full-length
posters on every street
corner and on hoardings
around construction sites
were perfectly superfluous; yet there
he was all over town, in hypnotic colours, eyes
blazing, magic wand tucked under his arm and chuckling away like
the Villain in a melodrama. Pictures of him were literally everywhere
along St. Catherine Street, between Morgan's and Place des Arts.

Boudini's New York show was still news a fortnight later. On
Broadway, the magician had been so successful at mystifying his
audiences that the municipal authorities, wary of his hypnotic effect
on the public, and even though minors were not admitted, finally
considered it necessary to issue him a warning.

A stenographer had fainted during his show when the great illusionist informed her she would surely die if she kept the appointment she had with an unlicensed obstetrician.

In addition to his magic feats, Boudini could see into the future;
this gift made him an extraordinary medium—a kind of prophet,
really. There was only one journalist who had dared try for an interview and he came away from it half mad. He promptly destroyed the
tape-recording he had made as well. Not to mention the fact that he
immediately afterwards consulted a psychiatrist.

The Society for the Protection of Holy Relics had protested vehemently about Boudini's Robespierre act, in which the magician appeared naked to the waist and held his head in his hands like Saint
Denis after his beheading. Both women and men swooned every
time at this horror. There had been nothing like it since Dracula.
The Society for the Protection of Holy Relics was so vociferous about

it that Boudini was finally compelled to cancel the act.

The Prince of Illusion—or the King of Horrors, as he was labelled by the suburban newspapers—came to Montreal for one night only. The next morning he took the plane for London where the Queen, in a special ceremony, was to make him a life member of an important British Order, in recognition of the seriousness he displayed in amusing his public.

The tickets were snapped up very quickly. Every last one of the one thousand three hundred and sixty-two seats was filled. The long-awaited moment finally arrived and Boudini appeared at the footlights in tie and tails.

It is customary for a professional conjurer to warm up with a few trifles. In Boudini's first trick, he pulled out the usual handkerchief which he handed to a girl in tights beside him. Out of the same pocket he then pulled a pillow-case, a wedding veil, a night-gown, a sheet, a superbly embroidered Egyptian carpet, and lastly a sail that two stage-hands and the girl in tights hoisted up on a mizzen-mast in the centre of the stage. The audience's applause was perfunctory. Someone even yelled out the supreme insult, "TRUQUEUR!" Boudini replied in French, "See here, Monsieur Tremblay, you earn an honest living selling shoes. Be so good as to let me earn *my* living *my* way." The shoe salesman was thunderstruck and sank down into his seat, not uttering another syllable.

Then, all alone on stage, the magician displayed a pack of cards and said: "Ladies and gentlemen; this pack is incomplete. The Queen of Hearts is missing. One of you out there has it. I ask that person to return it. Come now, look carefully. Still haven't found it? Well, well. I'll just have to take a hand. You, sir, in the fourth row. No, not you: the person sitting on your left. That's right. Would you mind returning my Queen of Hearts? Don't bother looking in your coat; it's in your wallet, between your son's picture and your daughter's. Very attractive girl, by the way. How old is she?"

With trembling hands the man finally produced the card from his wallet. This time the audience applauded generously.

Boudini continued, "I'm waiting, sir."

The man got up and stumbled over something in the aisle, which caused a great laugh at his expense. With mounting confusion, he approached the stage and handed the card to the magician who thanked him with, "Just a minute. Your wife is trying to get in touch with you." He snapped his fingers and the girl in tights brought forward a small table with a telephone on it.

"My wife?" gasped the man.

"I advise you to call her at once. I'm afraid she has some bad news for you."

A vast hush fell. The poor man picked up the receiver and dialled his home.

"Jean! That's right. From the theatre. It's a good thing I . . . . but why? Louise? What's wrong with her? But how? Wasn't the lid down? The doctor . . . . No, of course not; go right ahead. Take her to the hospital. I'm leaving right away."

He hung up and said to the magician, "You'll have to excuse me. My daughter had one of her hands crushed in the washing machine. Thanks for letting me know."

"I'm very sorry, sir, but no need to worry. She will be all right."

As the worried father made his way to the exit, a thrill of admiration rippled from one end of the theatre to the other.

Boudini then performed a series of short and brilliant feats of pure delight which he executed with simple elegance: pearls were cast before swine, omelettes were prepared without breaking an egg, the magician ate his cake and had it too, he robbed Peter to pay Paul, reaped as he had sown, and took a stitch in time to save nine.

While the stagehands were lugging out a ponderous armoire which they placed upstage, Boudini had a quick smoke in the wings. When he came back, he told his audience: "Once again I need your help, ladies and gentlemen. This time, however, I am calling upon the ladies only. Tell me now, is there someone here named Justine?"

A young girl rose. She was already in the aisle before Boudini could stop her.

"No, miss. Your name is Mary Elizabeth Justine. A very pretty name indeed, but I'm afraid I prefer just plain Justine. Kindly go back to your seat."

Bewildered and blushing, the girl did as she was told. The crowd murmured: "Unbelievable . . . incredible . . . utterly fantastic."

After the false Justine had resumed her seat, a woman in the first row raised her hand.

"Ah, madam. Do come forward." (She was a very attractive brunette with quick green eyes. She left her seat.) "You aren't afraid of me, are you?"

"Why should I be? I'm only afraid of men who are boring."

"Careful!" Boudini whispered, "You will arouse the enmity of too many men, my dear. And now," he said, turning to the audience, "someone whose name is Agnes."

Instantly, three women stood up at the same time.

"Now ladies, let's not get excited. Let me see.... You, for instance."

Boudini, being a man of taste, picked the most interesting of the three: enigmatic smile, half-closed eyes that mirrored flecks of malice, and the fire of a tigress. When she was beside him, Boudini asked her, "Aren't you rather nervous being this close to a terrifying man like me?"

"I've been around, you know. I don't really care, as long as there's fun to be had."

"You won't be disappointed, my dear. And now, isn't there another charming lady who is willing to come and play with us and whose name is Stephanie? Well? (A few seconds of silence.) Ah, there she is! There she is! Absolutely splendid. Do come forward, miss."

The girl's whole character was revealed in her easy stride and lack of self-consciousness. She was lively, gay; someone who obviously loved people and fun.

"I notice, miss, that you are not shy either. But why did you hesitate before coming up?"

"I was being silly. Then I said to myself: why not take advantage of the opportunity? It isn't every day the devil tempts you."

"You're a perfect angel."

The three women shook hands and began chatting. Then Boudini asked them to accompany him to the huge armoire. He opened the doors.

"After you, ladies."

The three women entered the armoire and Boudini closed the doors. He waved his hand and opened the doors again: the ladies had vanished. Boudini closed the armoire and came forward.

"And now let's get down to serious things," he said. His expression changed dramatically. He appeared to be concentrating. He stretched out his arms. A few minutes later every person in the first three rows was fast asleep. The snoring delighted the rest of the audience. With a gesture, the magician woke them up and seemed to enjoy the resulting confusion. Suddenly he looked up towards the ceiling and pointed dramatically to the chandelier. A perfectly useless but ornate half-ton mass, the chandelier at once began swaying ominously with a clinking and clashing like knights in battle. Screams rose from the audience directly below. Instantly, the pendular movement diminished until it stopped dead.

Some women in the audience were terribly frightened. As they were at the back of the theatre, they thought they could slip out without being seen. Unfortunately, the doors they were about to sneak through suddenly slammed in their faces. Everyone turned around to see what was happening. The women huddled around a pillar, breathless and shamefaced. The diabolical boldness of the magician had utterly petrified them and they just stood there, perfectly helpless.

"Ladies, please," said Boudini, "the show has hardly begun. You haven't seen anything yet."

So, very sheepishly, they went back to their seats while the audience giggled at them, feeling superior.

Boudini clapped his hands. A sharp bark in the wings was heard, and a Pomeranian dog appeared. Walking on its hind legs, it crossed the stage and stopped in front of its master, who leaned down and said, "What is Justine doing?"

"Justine?" replied the dog in a falsetto voice. "She's sleeping."

"And Agnes?"

"Agnes? She's sleeping."

"And Stephanie?"

"Stephanie? She's sleeping."

Pronunciation, accent, intonation: all flawless. The dog spoke English like a teacher of public speaking. The applause was long and appreciative.

"Tell me where the three of them are", said the magician.

"In the land of Nod," answered the dog.

Another burst of applause, and the animal raced off stage.

Boudini whistled. A donkey's braying was heard at once, and from the wings appeared a small, shaggy donkey who stopped dead in his tracks and would not move. He had a terrible case of stage fright.

"Come, come," said his master. "This isn't the time to put on airs."

The donkey trotted to the footlights and bowed. The magician scratched the animal's ears and asked, "What is your name?"

"Grizzle," the animal drawled.

"What would you like to do?"

"Sing."

"Sing what?"

"La donna."

"What 'donna'?"

"La donna è mobile."

"Please do, we are all ears."

And like a lead tenor, Grizzle sang the well-known aria from *Rigoletto*. This earned him long ripples of laughter.

"And now," said Boudini, "be nice and tell us what Justine is doing."

"Sleeping."

"And Agnes?"

"Sleeping."

"And Stephanie?"

"Sleeping."

"Where are all three of them?"

"In their beds."

To the amazed delight of the audience, the donkey spoke English like a learned linguist.

As soon as Grizzle had trotted out, Boudini clucked his tongue. There was a whinny from the wings and suddenly a splendid plough-horse appeared stage left. It capered about so elegantly that the audience went into raptures. Next, it nodded ceremoniously to everyone like a circus horse. Its coat was a brilliant scarlet and three large rubies glittered on its forehead. Boudini patted down a few tangles in the horse's mane and said, "Cincinattus, do tell me all you know about the three ladies you saw a little while ago. What are they doing?"

"They would be asleep for good, O Prince of Darkness, if you didn't have the power to waken them."

"Where are they?"

"In the grave."

The answer stunned everyone. So did the horse's impeccable diction. It was the first time that a horse had expressed himself before so many people with the perfection of a professor of English literature.

Boudini gave the horse a slap and off it galloped after bowing to the audience. The lights went out: ten seconds of darkness. Suddenly Boudini's face was lit up and then slowly his whole person. Now he was dressed in a lion-tamer's outfit. He cracked his long whip and the tip brushed against something that looked like reddish fur; it was still too dark to tell who or what was wearing it. Then suddenly another spotlight came on to reveal a very large lion. Everybody expected him to roar, so he obliged them; then all the stage lights came on.

Boudini stared at the lion which sprawled out and roared again, but this time with a vengeance. One woman turned a curious green and fainted instantly. She was taken out on a stretcher. People were muttering that the magician was going a little too far.

Still keeping an eye on the lion, Boudini tried to calm his audience.

"No need to get so upset, ladies and gentlemen, no need at all. Augustus is as gentle as a kitten. You will see in a minute. Augustus, what are you going to tell us today?"

"A fable," the lion boomed like a bass drum. The sound carried right out into the lobby.

"Which one?"

"The Animals Sick with the Plague."

"That's a little long. I suppose, though, that you want your customary share. Why can't you be satisfied with a short act like the dog, the donkey and the horse?"

"*Quia nominor leo.*"

"Ladies and gentlemen, do pardon me. I completely forgot to mention that Augustus is a polyglot. He also speaks French, but naturally English is his mother tongue."

The lion swished his tail back and forth, opened wide his mouth and began his fable.

"This awful scourge is a punishment . . . " and then he roared. "Now most justly by Heaven sent . . . " and he roared for the fourth time. The noise was so loud, however, that he spread terror throughout the theatre: men and women started rushing for the exits.

"Stop that, Augustus!" ordered Boudini, brandishing his whip. "Tell us instead where the three vanished ladies are."

Augustus got to his feet and went over to the armoire, sniffing at the doors. The lights went out for the second time. One last roar, though not as loud as the others, caused screams of panic in the darkness.

A spotlight flooded the armoire as its doors opened very slowly. Inside, standing upright, was a jet-black coffin. More lights came on, dimly illuminating other parts of the stage. Augustus could not be seen anywhere. Boudini and the two stage hands, with infinite precautions, removed the coffin from the armoire and set it down.

The stagehands left as soon as the coffin was in place. The audience was absolutely motionless. Boudini seemed to be concentrating. He raised his right arm. The girl in tights opened the coffin lid which grated on its hinges. Then she lit two tapers, one at the head of the black casket and the other at the foot. Then she backed away so discreetly that she seemed to melt into the shadows.

Boudini walked stiffly towards the coffin, spread his hands and called out in a loud voice, "Justine!"

Justine's head appeared. Her eyes were closed. Slowly the rest of the body was seen, shoulders, bust and waist. Standing there immobile in her coffin, she was perfectly beautiful, a kind of glow shimmering about her that was visible to everyone. A profound hush fell.

"Justine," said the magician, "where have you been?"

"In hell," answered the girl very slowly, without the slightest trace of emotion.

"Did you see anyone you know? Friends? Relatives?"

"I saw my husband and my two dead sons, drowned a year ago."

At this point a man in the audience lost his temper and began screaming, "This is scandalous. You haven't the right to make fun of people like that. Stop immediately."

The spoil-sport was promptly criticized by his neighbours for his sharpness, and an usher appeared to show him out of the theatre.

Boudini continued as though nothing had happened.

"Did you see other persons in hell?"

"I did."

"Who?"

"My father, his mistresses, an uncle, two aunts, a cousin."

"Would you name them if I asked you to?"

"Yes."

"Did you see any criminals there?"

"I did. A great many. Especially politicians. And popes."

"Name them."

Justine started to do so, but her voice was drowned out by shouts and boos. Boudini decided to cut some of his questions, thinking he had gone too far.

"Do you want to return to hell?"

"I do not."

"What must you do, then?"

"Crush the serpent."

And with these words she opened her eyes, stepped out of the coffin and came down to the footlights. She stiffened, holding her arms tightly by her sides.

Once again the magician spread out his hands above the coffin and called for Agnes. She appeared and answered a series of questions. The last was, "What must you do to be free?"

"Crush the serpent."

Boudini did have some trouble getting Stephanie to speak, once she had risen from the same coffin. Nevertheless, he asked her the same question, "What must you do to be free?"

"Crush the serpent."

The three women stood staring straight ahead, with a distance of about three yards between each. Boudini slipped into the wings for an instant and came back pushing a large hamper ahead of him. When he opened the lid, a rattlesnake emerged to the soft strains of Oriental music and slithered over to Justine.

People began screaming all over the theatre. In a split second the snake had coiled about Justine's body and reared its head like a question mark above her face. She struggled fiercely and managed to free her arms.

Out of the hamper glided a cobra and then an anaconda dragged its slow length along the floor. The cobra made for Agnes while the anaconda wrapped its enormous coils around Stephanie.

Boudini shouted over the din the audience was making, "If you say anything more, the girls will die."

Justine had the rattlesnake by the neck and squeezed it until the snake slowly relaxed its grip. Agnes had also released her arms and was busy wringing the cobra's neck like a wet rag. The startled snake slithered to the floor and lay there, motionless. That left Stephanie who was still struggling somewhere beneath the huge body of the anaconda. The girl in tights appeared and helped Stephanie to free herself. As she got to her feet she brought her heel down on the snake's head, which promptly played dead.

The snakes lay stretched out at the feet of the conquering girls. Boudini gave a command and the reptiles slipped back into the hamper.

The magician gestured, and his three collaborators instantly came out of their trance. They were roundly applauded even though they had no idea why the audience was so enthusiastic, since they could remember nothing. They were given a standing ovation and Boudini, who had upstaged himself for a moment, came back and stood beside them amid the cheers and shouts of the audience. With his upraised hand he asked for silence and instantly received it.

He shook hands with the girls, kissed them and joked a bit before turning to the audience.

"This evening," he said, " we have put on a great show thanks to our charming helpers here. I can now tell you that there was no little risk involved. I trust they will not refuse to dine with me after the show. Justine, what do you say?"

"Very gladly."

"Agnes?"

"With pleasure."

"And Stephanie?"

"Just as long as you don't put me to sleep again."

Laughter and applause as the curtain fell.

The theatre was invaded at intermission by reporters from the press, radio and television who had been tipped off by their colleagues in the audience. Armed with cameras and microphones, they interviewed people and filmed short sequences both inside and outside the theatre; they made a great fuss, especially about the ambulances parked in front of the main entrance.

Boudini, as usual, refused to give any interviews. When his dressing-room door was forced open, he ordered the intruders thrown out.

When the intermission was over and Boudini came out on stage, he demanded that the television cameras be removed from the aisles and he refused to begin his act until his orders were obeyed.

When things were to his liking once more, he decided to start off the second half of the show with a high-wire stunt, performing on a rope stretched well over twenty feet above the stage. On it, Boudini and his assistant balanced themselves, just beneath the overhead stage lights.

Next, he donned his magician's cape and looked exactly like his picture on the posters all over town. All that was missing was the top hat, which was handed to him by the girl in tights.

He went down into the orchestra pit, then back up to the footlights, making sure everyone had seen the silk hat. Then, moving upstage and holding the hat in one hand, he dipped the other hand inside and began stirring. At once dozens of wee white mice scampered out of the hat. They clambered up the magician's sleeve and onto his shoulders, scurried over his lapels, into his coat and down his trousers. He was smothered in them. Then he sneezed and they all vanished in a twinkling.

Next, out poured white rats from his silk hat, looking lost and confused. They huddled together in about thirty small groups on the stage. Then came repulsive sewer rats, huge brown things that the white rats chased into every corner possible. Women were screaming and standing paralyzed with fear or trying to run for the exits. The men held them back.

Then it was the rabbits' turn: three, four, five, ten, fifteen—twenty at least sprang from the hat and began jumping all over the floor, followed by a gaggle of leaping shrews. Three mongooses emerged and chased everything in sight. And finally a skunk bounded into the audience, causing quite a stir and a lot of laughs.

After the "mad menagerie", Boudini truly went to exceptional lengths to surpass himself.

"Ladies and gentlemen. Now that we have all had a good laugh, let us get down to more serious things."

He was handed a heavy, coarse outfit that looked like the uniform worn by executioners in the French Revolution. Apparently, he was about to give a new version of his Robespierre act.

The girl in tights and the stage hands came in carrying a real guillotine and a wicker basket. The instrument was set up and its mechanism verified.

Dressed like an executioner, Boudini turned to the audience.

"The authorities have forbidden me to request the assistance of anyone from the audience for the next act. Therefore I shall have to carry on alone with my faithful collaborator," and he pointed to the girl in tights.

She sat down on a stool next to the guillotine. The lights dimmed. Strange, insidious music stole across the mind and senses.

The "executioner" tapped his "victim" on the shoulder. She rose and Boudini removed the stool, telling her to kneel down. As the girl did so, the magician loosened the bolts holding together the two half-circles of the lunette and spread them apart. He then brushed aside the girl's hair, exposing her neck. She leaned forward and put her head down, which was held firmly in place as he lowered the top half of the lunette onto the bottom half. The anxiety in the air was stifling. Boudini walked around the instruments of torture as the lights came up in harsh, garish colours. The audience was spellbound, actually convinced they were witnessing an execution during the Reign of Terror. Boudini released the blade. A dull thump was heard. The head of the dead girl tumbled into the basket and blood spurted from her neck.

The King of Horrors had never dared spill blood in his acts before this, and its effect was electrifying. Five or six persons who took the whole thing too seriously could not stand it and fainted from fright. They were carried to the street where they were cared for by the nurses standing by. The theatre was in a total uproar. Strong, even violent protests were raised. And in the midst of the confusion the lights went out. The protests grew even more violent until the lights came back on to reveal Boudini next to his assistant, both of them smiling and bowing. Some persons in the audience, however, were not to be appeased by this reassuring sight: some of them, who were disgusted with the whole thing, had called the police.

When two policemen arrived soon afterwards, the audience finally calmed down, wondering what was going to happen next. The good constables started up the aisle towards the stage. When Boudini asked them their business, they ignored him.

When they got to the orchestra pit and were about to go up to the magician on stage, they suddenly stood stock still as though paralyzed. Boudini gestured and they suddenly came back to life. This little trick won the audience over, and good humour returned at once. The constables, however, had received orders after all and chose to ignore Boudini's warning as they walked up on stage to speak to him. The magician pretended to give them his undivided attention but as they were speaking, an invisible hand whisked off their jackets. The policemen seemed perfectly oblivious to what was happening as their shirts and ties also vanished. People were now laughing uproariously, completely on Boudini's side and pleased they could make fun of the police and get away with it. The two policemen were now clad in nothing but their underwear tops and trousers, and by the time the latter had slipped down around their hips and seemed about to slither even farther, the audience's joy knew no bounds. The guillotine and all its gore were forgotten.

When their trousers finally dropped around their ankles, Boudini thought it advisable to point out to them the near-indecent state of their dress—or undress. The policemen exploded in fury when they finally realized what had happened and reached out to grab Boudini, but some force held them back. After a few vain attempts, their anger gave way to fright and they took off, clad only in their shorts, and vanished through a side door.

There was an instant explosion of laughter in which all the variations of the human temperament could be heard: a chaotic mass of human sounds, low, medium, high-pitched; a prolonged dissonance interspersed with frenzied whistling. This cacophony gradually melded into a single rhythm, one vast wave of laughter that rolled back and forth throughout the theatre. Some people fell out of their seats and sprawled in the aisles; others staggered to the lobby in a frantic search for a little fresh air; some even had to be slapped so they would not choke to death.

The stage manager ordered all house lights on, and this brought a little calm back to the theatre, but not much. Just enough for the reporters to take advantage of the relative quiet to try and interview Boudini. They really believed the show was over. But this attempt also failed.

Boudini's assistant came forward and announced the last act; Boudini had retired to the wings; the stage was cleared of all unnecessary props.

When Boudini appeared at last, he received an ovation that lasted almost a minute.

He lit a cigarette; with the cigarette he lit a cigar; with the cigar he lit a torch, then two torches, a third, a fourth, a fifth and a sixth. The master illusionist began juggling the torches and they made a fiery wheel on the darkened stage. He handed all the torches but one to his assistant and with it he proceeded to describe a circle of fire on the floor. The flames blazed up and Boudini walked through them and stood in the centre of the circle. The flames leaped higher and higher.

Smoke began pouring into the theatre in greyish spark-filled spirals like the phosphorescent clouds sometimes seen during a storm. The discomfort in the audience was very real; people started coughing and some even left for good, quite fed up with the whole thing. The stage manager—who had taken refuge in the prompter's box and who, in his career in the theatre, had seen many a peculiar sight —was making desperate signs to Boudini, absolutely convinced that the magician was stark, raving mad to risk setting the whole theatre on fire.

By now the theatre was more than half empty; only a few very hardy souls remained, and they saw Boudini's whole person catch fire. Blazing like a torch, he extended a fiery hand to the girl in tights and together they both stepped into the circle of flames. Fire curled out of his eyes, mouth, nose and ears. As he drew the girl closer to him the flames raced through her body as well. Then suddenly, as though snuffed out by a huge blast of air, the fires were extinguished and the smoke vanished. And with his assistant in his arms the Prince of Illusion rose slowly towards the ceiling in a feat of levitation that was the climax of the show.

People raced up on stage, crowded in front of it, and even rushed into the streets. The stage manager climbed to the upper flies, but to no avail. Boudini and his assistant had vanished without a trace.

The firemen arrived, but since there was no fire anywhere the officer in charge threatened to take legal action against the management.

In Dominion Square, Boudini's three friends—Justine, Agnes and Stephanie—had tired of waiting for the magician and were just about to go their separate ways when Boudini's Bentley pulled up beside them.

They were overjoyed to see him and got into his car, thrilled that he had kept his promise to meet them after the show.

They spent part of the night in a big night club on Sherbrooke Street, where the four of them had a great time together; the burgundy had body and the champagne had spirit. And yet, never once did the Master of Illusion answer any question about the secrets of his art. Boudini was a man of the world and as such had adopted the rule of never talking shop at table.

The manager of the theatre came home after the show to find the following telegram on his desk:

LONDON. 15/8/64. REQUEST EXPLANATION ABOUT RUMOURS CONCERNING ME IN MONTREAL STOP LAID UP HERE EIGHT DAYS AFTER BAD FALL STOP HAVE NEVER BEEN TO MONTREAL STOP HAVE NEVER SIGNED CONTRACT FOR SHOW IN YOUR THEATRE STOP IMMEDIATE REPLY REQUESTED STOP REGARDS.

SIGNED: BOUDINI

Roch Carrier

The Bird
The Ink
Creation

Roch Carrier is probably the best known young Quebec writer in English Canada. His trilogy, *La Guerre, Yes Sir!, Floralie, Where are you?* and *Is it the Sun, Philibert?*, translated by Sheila Fischman, has sold better west of Ottawa than the original did at home. Thousands of students have read at least part of this sardonic history of our paradoxical times. *La Guerre, Yes Sir!* was produced in an English version at the Stratford Festival and has now been made into a film

Less well known are his short stories which appeared under the title *Jolis Deuils: Petites tragédies pour adultes*, in 1964. At that time, Carrier, who was twenty-seven, provided the following biographical notes:

"Carrier was a nickname in the beginning, given to my ancestors because they were church-builders.

On a sun-drenched island an uncle of mine lived for seven years on goat's milk waiting for his first orange crop.

A cousin who hadn't a cent to his name undertook to dig a tunnel to join two cities on opposite banks of the St. Lawrence

I'm in love

I'm happy

I'm a compulsive liar.

In *Jolis Deulis* I tell nothing but the unvarnished truth."

Sheila Fischman is one of the founders of *Ellipse*, the quarterly review of Canadian poetry in translation. She has translated all Carrier's novels, Fernand Dumont's *La Vigile du Québec*, and is currently working on *Le Loup* by Marie-Claire Blais.

The Bird

One day a swallow came
to announce the arrival of
spring. Its flight was jovous, its soul
filled with delight at what was to come.
Then it bumped its head against a wall of wind and fell into the middle of the town's public square.

The next day was exceptionally cold. Cars refused to start. The river was covered with ice. Streets were deserted. People who were brave enough to go out were forced back inside by the piercing cold.

Newspaper headlines lyrically described its fierceness. The papers were distributed all over town but nobody bought them.

The radio announced that such severe cold had never before been registered in the meteorological records. It suggested caution.

Buses stayed in the garage and trains in the station, iron beasts huddled against one another, numb. Traffic lights at deserted intersections stalled on red.

The radio urged extreme care.

In their houses, people eating breakfast were as happy as schoolchildren given a surprise holiday. You could hear a small dry sound, like singing crystal: a fine dusting of ice had covered the coffee. The bread had hardened on the plates.

The radio announced that dozens of vagrants had been found on the subway's air vents, frozen.

Electric lights went out. Faces, walls, everything was impregnated with the sombre colour of the sky. The radio announced that a troop of soldiers ordered to march around the town had perished.

People were bundled up in sweaters, coats, blankets. Houses crackled. Windows shattered.

The radio, which had been broadcasting soft music, was suddenly silent.

Little by little the flames ceased dancing on the hearths. They stopped moving altogether, congealed, with the livid appearance of melted wax. You could touch it. It made a noise like crumpling paper. Children tore off bits of it and put them in their mouths. The taste was like cold tea.

Some people still wanted to speak. But they could no longer be heard. The sound clung to their lips. Their mouths had become stiffened rings.

Those whose eyelids were not sealed noticed a strange phenomenon: in the walls there was no longer any plaster or stones or bricks or wood. Everything was ice. Those who could still move touched it. It gave off warmth like the body of a woman. They crawled along the translucent walls.

Their flesh became transparent. Their hearts could be seen, like motionless red fish. Eventually their bodies crumbled with a tinkling sound.

Then nothing more happened. But a small red flower was quivering in the middle of the public square.

The Ink

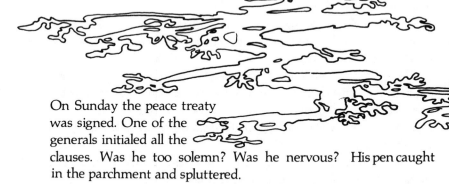

On Sunday the peace treaty
was signed. One of the
generals initialed all the
clauses. Was he too solemn? Was he nervous? His pen caught
in the parchment and spluttered.

The general looked at the stains on his fingers. Helpless, he also
watched the blob of ink spread across the page. Slowly the parchment drank up the ink. The general was escorted to the sink, but the
ink resisted water. He came back to distribute handshakes, proud
that peace had been signed.

The stain spread. Half the parchment was blackened. Signatures
and part of the text of the treaty were flooded with ink. Soon the
whole parchment was solid black.

When it was time to close the building the stain had spread beyond
the edges of the document and was pursuing its proud course onto
the table. The caretaker closed the shutters, bolted the door, clomped
down ten corridors and headed for the bistro.

When he arrived on Monday the stain had taken over the rugs,
the walls, the ceiling. It had asserted its presence on the chandeliers
and windows. The panic-stricken caretaker closed the door and bar-
ricaded it. Useless. The ink crept along the corridors and slid beneath
the doors. No brush, no soap was effective in barring its passage. By
evening it had invaded the building's most secret corners.

The fire brigade, the police, the army, the ditch-diggers and the
dam-builders were called out. They circled the building. But the ink
triumphed over their dedication and initiative. After taking on the
streets of the town, it took over the parks, tinted the water in the
fountains and changed the colour of the chestnut trees and their
leaves.

As the stain spread it became more ravenous. On Tuesday not a
single house had been spared by the black ink. It even crowned the

tall cathedral spire. The entire town seemed to have been dipped in an immense inkwell.

On Wednesday news arrived from neighbouring towns, announcing that the ink was approaching. The wheat in the fields was stained black and so was the grass. The animals' feet were beginning to blacken. The ink was climbing up the foundations of the houses. The stain spread with the speed of a hurricane. That day the black fury completed its occupation of the entire country.

On Thursday it crossed the borders. The invasion began. Patriots declared war on the invader. Nations joined together the better to tear each other apart: fires, bombardments, explosions, blood.

On Friday: fires, bombardments, explosions, blood.

Pitiless, the ink extended its empire. Its shadow hovered over ten countries. Soon the sea would give in too. Fighting became futile. But they continued for a while, for the sake of honour. On Saturday, very late, the cease-fire was ordered.

The peace treaty was signed the following Sunday. One of the generals initialed all the clauses. Was he too solemn? Was he nervous? His pen caught in the parchment and spluttered.

Creation

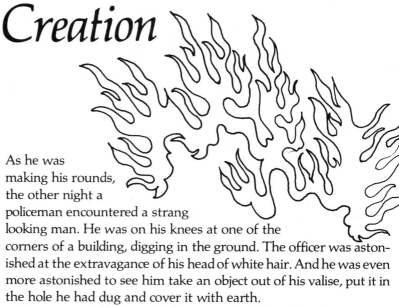

As he was
making his rounds,
the other night a
policeman encountered a strang
looking man. He was on his knees at one of the
corners of a building, digging in the ground. The officer was astonished at the extravagance of his head of white hair. And he was even
more astonished to see him take an object out of his valise, put it in
the hole he had dug and cover it with earth.

The man got up then, displaying an abundant beard.

At the next corner of the building he began to dig again. Again he
buried something. The officer, amused and intrigued, did not take his
eyes off the man.

After repeating his tour around the building several times, the
man seemed to reflect for a moment, to calculate. Finally he made his
decision and hid his valise behind a bush. Then he returned to the
first hole and made motions as if he were tying something.

In his long gown the man resembled God the Father; the officer
found it hard to keep from laughing.

For several minutes the man went back and forth between the
building and the bush, all the time unwinding a string behind him.
The officer, in his thick-skulled way, concluded that he was playing
some kind of idiotic game. Perhaps he was mooring the building to
the bush? The officer was amused.

The man dived into the honeysuckle and didn't come out again. A
sudden headache made the officer stagger. Paralyzed by a stone that
had hurled him to the ground, he wanted to call for help. His jaw was
welded shut.

In the meantime the building had blown up, burst like a toy
balloon.

Soon after, the patriarch was arrested. In his hand he was holding a valise that contained delicate explosives and brilliant detonators. He was taken and put behind bars with no ceremony whatsoever.

They shaved him and cut his hair, gave him a shirt, a pair of trousers and a jacket. In his original costume he had looked like an imbecile, and one was prepared to forgive him anything. Now that he looked like an honest employee, he was as good as sentenced.

"What is your name?"

"God," replied the formerly bearded man.

His papers were checked and proved that he spoke the truth.

"You can explain yourself to the Judge!"

After waiting for weeks in a damp dark cell that stank infernally, God was summoned by the Judge. How God regretted that he had created his flowers, his sky, and his cushions of cloud, only to be deprived of them.

The Judge spoke to him good-naturedly:

"Really, God, you amaze me!"

God answered with a question:

"Your Honour, are you happy with your life on earth?"

"Indeed I am," replied the Judge with delight. His young secretary had finally agreed to a rendezvous.

"You really do like this good little earth?" God went on.

"I couldn't live anywhere else," declared the Judge.

"Do you know," God continued, "that this pretty little earth was born out of an explosion that I set off with my hands?"

Despite the wisdom of his plea God was sentenced to seven years of solitary confinement, during which they tried to teach him how peaceful citizens should behave.

That was seven years ago. God's hair grew long again, his beard regained its majesty. That is why, some foggy evening, you might well see a strange-looking man digging at the corner of some building.

Hubert Aquin

Back on April Eleven

Hubert Aquin (b. 1929) is a member of that trio of brilliant young writers who best characterize Quebec fiction in the 'sixties, the other two being Marie-Claire Blais and Réjean Ducharme. He is the most sophisticated of the three, the most contemporary. His three main novels to date, *Prochain Episode* (1965), *Trou de Mémoire* (1968), and *L'Antiphonaire* (1969), have partly international settings, their subjects are drugs, revolution, and murder, and their experiments in language and form recall Alain Resnais, Kafka and Joyce.

The story included here, which the author refers to as "my best and probably my last short story", is not particularly experimental—perhaps Aquin needs more space for that—but it does exemplify his brand of suave, racy, slightly vertiginous fiction. The slithering drive back from the airport, the deadening effects of snow over Montreal, the elaborate suicide preparations and the narrator's prevailing irony have psycho-political connotations which give the story an added dimension.

Alan Brown, who now works for the CBC in Montreal, is the distinguished translator of two novels by the French writer Blaise Cendrars, *Moravagine*, and *Emmène-moi au bout du monde*. He has also translated two Quebec novels, *Salut Galarneau* by Jacques Godbout and *L'Antiphonaire* by Hubert Aquin.

Back on April Eleventh

When your
letter came I
was reading a Mickey
Spillane. I'd already been
interrupted twice, and was having
trouble with the plot. There was this
man Gardner, who for some reason always carted around the photo
of a certain corpse. It's true I was reading to kill time. Now I'm not so
interested in killing time.

It seems you have no idea of what's been going on this winter.
Perhaps you're afflicted with a strange intermittent amnesia that
wipes out me, my work, our apartment, the brown record-player....
I assure you I can't so easily forget this season I've passed without
you, these long, snowy months with you so far away. When you left
the first snow had just fallen on Montreal. It blocked the sidewalks,
obscured the houses and laid down great pale counterpanes in the
heart of the city.

The evening you left—on my way back from Dorval—I drove
aimlessly through the slippery empty streets. Each time the car went
into a skid I had the feeling of going on an endless voyage. The Mustang was transformed into a rudderless ship. I drove for a long time
without the slightest accident, not even a bump. It was dangerous
driving, I know. Punishable by law. But that night even the law had
become a mere ghost of itself, as had the city and this damned mountain that we've tramped so often. So much whiteness made a strong
impression on me. I remember feeling a kind of anguish.

You, my love, probably think I'm exaggerating as usual and that I
get some kind of satisfaction out of establishing these connections
between your leaving and my states of mind. You may think I'm
putting things together in retrospect in such a way as to explain what
happened after that first fall of cerusian white.

But you're wrong: I'm doing nothing of the kind. That night, I tell you, the night you left, I skidded and slipped on that livid snow, fit to break your heart. It was myself I lost control of each time the Mustang slid softly into the abyss of memory. Winter since then has armed our city with many coats of melting mail, and here I am already on the verge of a burnt-ivory spring. . . .

Someone really has to tell you, my love, that I tried twice to take my life in the course of this dark winter.

Yes, it's the truth. I'm telling you this without passion, with no bitterness or depths of melancholy. I'm a little disappointed at having bungled it; I feel like a failure, that's all. But now I'm bored. I've fizzled out under the ice. I'm finished.

Have you, my love, changed since last November? Do you still wear your hair long? Have you aged since I saw you last? How do you feel about all this snow that's fallen on me, drifting me in? I suppose a young woman of twenty-five has other souvenirs of her travels besides these discoloured postcards I've pinned to the walls of our apartment?

You've met women . . . or men; you've met perhaps one man and . . . he seemed more charming, more handsome, more "liberating" than I could ever be. Of course, as I say that, I know that to liberate oneself from another person one has only to be unfaithful. In this case you were right to fly off to Amsterdam to escape my black moods; you were right to turn our liaison into a more relative thing, the kind that other people have, any old love affair, any shabby business of that kind. . . .

But that's all nonsense. I'm not really exaggerating, I'm just letting myself go, my love, letting myself drift. A little like the way I drove the Mustang that night last November. I'm in distress, swamped by dark thoughts. And it's no use telling myself that my imagination's gone wild, that I'm crazy to tell you these things, for I feel that this wave of sadness is submerging both of us and condemning me to total desolation. I can still see the snowy streets and me driving through them with no rhyme or reason, as if that aimless motion could magically make up for losing you. But, you know, I already had a sedimentary confused desire to die, that very evening.

While I was working out the discords of my loneliness at the steering wheel of the Mustang, you were already miles high in a DC-8 above the North Atlantic. And a few hours later your plane would land gently on the icy runway of Schipol—after a few leisurely manoeuvres over the still plains of the Zuider Zee. By then I would be back in our apartment, reading a Simenon—*The Nahour Affair*—set partly in a Paris blanketed in snow (a rare occurrence), but also in that very city of Amsterdam where you had just arrived. I went to sleep in the small hours of the morning, clutching that bit of reality that somehow reconnected me to you.

The next day was the beginning of my irreversible winter. I tried to act as if nothing had changed and went to my office at the Agency (Place Ville Marie) at about eleven. I got through the day's work one way or another. While I was supposed to be at lunch I went instead to the ground-floor pharmacy. I asked for phenobarbital. The druggist told me, with a big stupid grin, that it called for a prescription. I left the building in a huff, realizing, however, that this needed a little thought.

I had to have a prescription, by whatever means, and information about brand-names and doses. And I needed at least some knowledge of the various barbiturate compounds.

With this drug very much on my mind I went next day or the day after to the McGill medical bookstore. Here were the shelves dealing with pharmacology. I was looking for a trickle and found myself confronted by the sea. I was overcome, submerged, astonished. I made a choice and left the store with two books under my arm: the *Shorter Therapeutics and Pharmacology*, and the *International Vade Mecum* (a complete listing of products now on the market).

That night, alone with my ghosts, I got at the books. To hell with Mickey Spillane, I had better things to read: for example, this superbook (the *Vade Mecum*) which has the most delicious recipes going! Your appetite, your tensions, your depressions—they are all at the command of a few grams of drugs sagely administered. And according to this book of magic potions, life itself can be suppressed if only one knows how to go about it. I was passionately engrossed by this flood of pertinent information, but I still had my problem of how to get a prescription. Or rather, how to forge one that wouldn't turn into a passport to prison. A major problem.

His name was in the phone book: Olivier, J.R., internist. I dialled his number. His secretary asked what would be the best time of day for an appointment and specified that it would be about a month as the

doctor was very busy. I answered her with a daring that still surprises me:

"It's urgent."

"What is it you have?" asked the secretary.

"A duodenal ulcer."

"How do you know?"

"Well, I've consulted several doctors and they strongly advised me
to see Doctor O."

"Tomorrow at eleven," she suggested, struck by my argument.
"Will that be convenient?"

"Of course," I replied.

I spent forty-five minutes in the waiting room with the secretary
I'd phoned the day before. I flipped through the magazines on the
table searching for subjects of conversation to use on this doctor
friend I hadn't seen for so long.

He appeared in the doorway and his secretary murmured my
name. I raised my gloomy gaze to greet this smiling friend. He ush-
ered me into his overstuffed office.

After the usual halting exchange of memories from college and
university days I took a deep breath and, talking directly to Olivier,
J.R., I told him straight out that I was having trouble sleeping. He
burst into laughter, while I crouched deeper in the armchair he kept
for patients.

"You're living it up too much, old boy," he said, smiling.

Just then his intercom blinked. Olivier lifted the phone.

"What is it?" he asked his secretary.

(I had been hoping for something like this.)

"Just a second. I have something to sign. You know how it is.
They're making bureaucrats out of us."

He got up and went out to the reception room, carefully closing
the door. At once I spied on his hand-rest the prescription pad with
his letterhead. I quickly tore off a number of sheets and stuck them in
the left inside pocket of my jacket. I was trembling, dripping with
sweat.

"Well, bring me up to date," said Olivier, coming back. "Is she running around on you?"

He obviously found his own humour as irresistible as I found it
offensive and our chat didn't get much farther. We fell silent and
Olivier took his pen. Before starting to write on his prescription pad
he looked up at me.

"What was it, now? You wanted some barbiturates to get you to sleep?"

"Yes," I said.

"Okay, here's some stuff that'll knock out a horse." He tore off the sheet and held it out to me.

"Thanks, thank you very much." I suppose I was a bit emotional.

"I've put *non repetatur* at the bottom for these pills have a tendency to be habit-forming. If you really need more after a couple of weeks come and see me again."

I folded the prescription without even searching out the *non repetatur*, an expression I had learned only a couple of days before. The intercom blinked again. Olivier, annoyed, picked up his phone but I paid no attention. I was already far away. Afterwards Olivier started telling me how his wife complained—or so he said—that she never got to see him any more.

"I'm working too hard," he said, hand on brow. "I probably need a holiday, but there it is. My wife's the one who's off to Europe. And it's only a month or so since she did the Greek Islands."

In my mind I saw you in the streets of Breda and The Hague. I imagined your walks in Scheveningen, your visits to the Maurithuis. I wasn't sure any more just where in Europe you were: at the Hook of Holland, the flying isle of Vlieland, or the seaside suburb of Leiden, at Kalwijk aan Zee. . . .

I was out again on the chilly street. The sky was dark and lowering. Black clouds scudded by at rooftop level, presaging another snowstorm. Let the snow come to beautify this death-landscape, where I drove in a Mustang while you moved in the clear celestial spaces of the painters of the Dutch school. . . .

Back in our apartment I analyzed the prescription I had obtained by trickery. Twelve capsules of sodium amobarbital. I had no intention of remaining the possessor of a non-repeatable number of pills and began practising Olivier's handwriting. On ordinary paper. I had stolen ten sheets of his letterhead but that precious paper must not be wasted. In two or three hours I'd managed four good prescriptions. I fell asleep on the strength of my success.

It took me some days to accumulate a *quoad vitam* dose with the help of my forged scribbles. But I wasn't satisfied with the *quoad vitam* dose indicated in the *Vade Mecum*. I went on accumulating the little sky-blue capsules, each with its three-letter stamp—SK&F.

There were nights when I slept not at all rather than dip into my stock of precious sodic torpedoes.

Quite a few days passed this way. Strange days. Knowing that I had my stock of death in hand I felt sure of myself and almost in harmony with life. I knew that I was going to die and at that moment it would have been upsetting to receive a letter from you, my love, for I had come too close to the end of living.

When your letter came on November sixteenth it in no way disturbed this harmony, as I had feared it might. After reading it I still wanted to end my life by using, some evening, my surprising accumulation of sodium amobarbital. You'd written in haste (I could tell by your hand) from the Amstel Hotel, but the postmark said Utrecht. So you'd mailed it from there! What were you doing in Utrecht? How had you gone from Amsterdam to that little town where the treaty was signed ratifying the conquest of French Canada? Symbol of the death of a nation, Utrecht became a premonitory symbol of my own death. Had you gone with someone? A European colleague, as you usually describe the men you meet on your travels? Are there many interior decorators in Utrecht? Or perhaps I should ask if they are friendly and charming. I imagined you sitting in the car of a decorator colleague, lunching on the way and perhaps spending the night in Utrecht. I grew weary of calling back so many memories of you, your charm, your beauty, your hot body in my arms. I tore up your letter to put an end to my despair.

By the twenty-eighth of November I'd heard nothing more from you. My days grew shorter and emptier, my nights longer and more sleepless. They finally seemed barely to be interrupted by my days and I was exhausted. Recurrent insomnia had broken my resistance. I was destroyed, hopeless, without the slightest will to organize what was left of my life.

For me an endless night was about to begin, the unique, final, ultimate night. I'd at last decided to put an arbitrary end to my long hesitation, a period to our disordered history; decided, also, no longer to depend on your intermittent grace, which had been cruel only in that I had suffered from it.

That day I made a few phone calls to say I was not available and spent my time tidying the apartment. When it was evening I took a very hot bath copiously perfumed from the bottle of Seaqua. I soaked for a long time in that beneficent water. Then I put on my burnt-orange bathing trunks and piled a few records on our playback: Ray Charles, Feliciano, Nana Mouskouri. I sprawled on our scarlet sofa, a glass of Chivas Regal in my hand, almost naked, fascinated by the total void that was waiting for me. I put Nana Mouskouri on several times. Then I finally made up my mind and swallowed my little sky-blue capsules four at a time, washing them down with great gulps of Chivas Regal. At the end I took more Scotch to help me absorb the lot. I put the nearly empty bottle on the rug just beside the couch. Still quite lucid, I turned on the radio (without getting up) so that the neighbours would not be alerted by the heavy breathing which, according to my medical sources, would begin as soon as I dropped into my coma.

To tell you the truth I wasn't sad but rather impressed, like someone about to start a long, very long, voyage. I thought of you, but faintly, oh, so faintly. You were moving around in the distance, in a funereal fog. I could still see the rich colours of your dresses and bathrobes. I saw you enter the apartment like a ghost and leave it in slow-motion, but eternally in mirror perspective leading to infinity. The deeper I slipped into my comatose feast the less you looked my way, or rather the less I was conscious of you. Melancholy had no grip on me, nor fear. In fact I was blanketed in the solemnity of my solitude. Then, afterwards, obliteration became less complex and I became mortuary but not yet dead, left rocking in a total void.

And now, you ask, how are you managing to write this letter from beyond the tomb?

Well, here's the answer: I failed! The only damage I received in this suicide attempt resulted from the coma that lasted several hours. I was not in the best of condition. My failure—even if I had no other devastating clues—would be proof enough of my perfect weakness, that diffuse infirmity that cannot be classified by science but which allows me to ruin everything I touch, always, without exception.

I woke up alive, as it were, in a white ward of the Royal Victoria, surrounded by a network of intravenous tubes that pinned me to the bed and ringed by a contingent of nurses. My lips felt frozen and dried and I remember that one of the nurses sponged my lips from time to time with an anti-herpetic solution.

Outside it was snowing, just as it had been on the day you left. The great white flakes fell slowly and I became aware that the very fact of seeing them silently falling was irrefutable proof that I was still, and horridly, alive. My return to a more articulated consciousness was painful, and took (to my relief) an infinity. As soon as I reached that threshold of consciousness I began to imagine you in the Netherlands or somewhere in Europe. Was there snow in Holland? And did you need your high suede boots that we shopped for together a few days before you left?

Suddenly I feel a great fatigue: these thoughts, returning in all their disorder, are taking me back to my stagnant point again. . . .

It was really quite ironic that your telegram from Bruges should have become the means of your tardy (and involuntary) intervention on behalf of my poisoned body. I suppose the message was phoned first. But I didn't hear the ring and Western Union simply delivered the typed message to my address. The caretaker, who has no key to the letter boxes in our building, felt the call of duty and decided to bring me the envelope himself. There is something urgent about telegrams, you can't just leave them lying around. People can't imagine a harmless telegram that might read: HAPPY BIRTHDAY. WEATHER MARVELLOUS. KISSES. And yet that's exactly what was written in that telegram from Bruges.

I suppose the caretaker rapped a few times on our door. He probably couldn't see how I'd be out when the radio was blasting away. Finally, his curiosity must have got the better of him. He opened the door with his pass-key and stepped in to leave the envelope on the Louis XV table under the hall mirror. It's easy to imagine the rest: from the door he saw that I was there, he noted my corpse-like face, etc. Then, in a panic, he phoned the Montreal Police who transported me—no doubt at breakneck speed—to the emergency ward of the Royal Victoria. I spent several days under an oxygen tent. I even underwent a tracheotomy. That, in case the term means nothing to you, involves an incision in the trachea, followed by the insertion of a tracheal drain.

I must tell you everything, my love. I'm alive, therefore I am cured. The only traces are an immense scar on my neck and a general debility. While I was surviving one way or another in Montreal, you were continuing your tour of Europe. You saw other cities, Brussels, Charleroi, Amiens, Lille, Roubaix, Paris. . . . Bruges had been just a stopover where you perhaps had dinner with a stranger, but no one hangs around in Bruges when the continent is waiting. Though God knows Bruges is a privileged place, an amorous sanctuary, a fortress that has given up a little terra firma to the insistent North Sea. I feel a soft spot for that half-dead city which you left with no special feeling. I stayed on in Bruges after you left, immured beneath its old and crumbling quays, for that was where you wished me (by telegram) a happy birthday.

There is no end to this winter. I don't know how many blizzards I watched from my hospital window. Around the fifteenth of December some doctor decided I should go home, that I was—so to speak—cured. Easy to say! Can one be cured of having wanted to die? When the ambulance attendants took me up to the apartment I saw myself in a mirror. I though I would collapse. As a precaution I lay down on the couch where I had almost ended my days in November. Nothing had changed since then, but there was a thin film of dust on our furniture and the photos of you. The sky, lowering and dark, looked like more snow. I felt like a ghost. My clothes hung loose on me and my skin had the colour of a corpse. The sleepless nights again took up their death march but I no longer had my reserve of suicide-blue amobarbital pills. And I'd used up all my blank prescription forms. I couldn't sleep. I stared at the ceiling or at the white snowflakes piling up on our balcony. I imagined you at Rome or Civitavecchia or in the outskirts of Verona, completely surrendered to the intense experience of Europe.

From my calendar I knew that you were coming back to Montreal on April eleventh, on board the *Maasdam*. If I went to meet you that day at the docks of the Holland-American Line I would be in an emotional state. Too emotional, unable to tell you about what I did in November or about my disintegration since. Of course you'd give me a great hug and tell me all about those marvels, the fascinating ruins in Bruges, the baths of Caracalla, the Roman arches of triumph: the Arch of Tiberius, of Constantine, of Trajan, and so on. And all through your euphoric monologue I'd feel the knot at my throat.

It's for that reason—and all sorts of others, all somehow related to cowardice—that I'm writing you this letter, my love. I'll soon finish it and address it to Amsterdam, from which the *Maasdam* sails, so that you can read it during the crossing. That way you'll know that I bungled my first suicide attempt in November.

You'll understand that if I say "first" it means there'll be a second.

Don't you see that my hand is trembling? That my writing is beginning to scrawl? I'm already shaky. The spaces between each word, my love, are merely the symbols of the void that is beginning to accept me. I have ten more lucid minutes, but I've already changed: my mind is slipping, my hand wanders, the apartment, with every light turned on, grows dark where I look. I can barely see the falling snow but what I do see is like blots of ink. My love, I'm shivering with cold. The snow is falling somehow within me, my last snowfall. In a few seconds, I'll no longer exist, I will move no more. And so I'm sorry but I won't be at the dock on April eleventh. After these last words I shall crawl to the bath, which has been standing full for nearly an hour. There, I hope, they will find me, drowned. Before the eleventh of April next.

Marie-Claire Blais

The New Schoolmistress

Marie-Claire Blais became famous in 1966 when, at the age of twenty-seven, she won the important French literary prize, Le Prix Medicis for *A Season in the Life of Emmanuel.* This was already her sixth book and she has published a novel a year since, her latest, *Un joualonais, sa joualonie,* closest in style and quality to *Emmanuel.*

It is unfortunate, at least for this collection, that such a prolific writer should have published so few short stories. One or two have appeared but they are disappointing. So to represent her we include here not a short story but an extract from an unpublished novel planned to be a sequel to *A Season in the Life of Emmanuel* and provisionally entitled *Le Testament de Jean Le Maigre.* Although it is an excerpt, the passage is self-contained and shows Marie-Claire Blais writing at the top of her form. It also illustrates well her range of vision, which is at once ghoulish and grotesque, humorous, satirical and compassionate.

Vida Bruce has a B.A. in French and German from Toronto and an M.A. in French-Canadian Literature from McMaster. She is presently translating the nineteenth century Quebec classic, *Jean Rivard,* by Antoine Gérin-Lajoie.

The New Schoolmistress

"Where does
he live, this here
school inspector?"
Judith Prunelle asked
Abbé Philippe Rougemont, who was shaking out his cassock
with one hand and pulling his bicycle out of the ditch with the other.
"Jesus Christ, I'm lost!"

"Lower your voice," said the Abbé, "I'm not deaf."

And that was how the new mistress of the School of Repentance
entered this godforsaken village. (The absence of a teacher for the
last three years had forced the Abbé to teach the children their catechism at home, an undertaking he had found both disappointing
and ineffectual since not a single family welcomed him, with the
exception of Grand'mère Antoinette. And even she, probably hoping
to conceal the depths of her poverty, received the Abbé on the doorstep trying to stop up the gaps in her household by placing her long
stern silhouette on the stoop in front of him as if to forbid his entrance, imagining that the wall of shadow it created would hide the
dearth within.) "Oh dear God! What kind of teacher is this you're
sending us?" thought the Abbé, staring at the young girl who stood
there in the middle of the road, a battered suitcase in her hand, saying
in her rough slang, "Jesus, Mary and Joseph, where've I landed?"
Descended from heaven no doubt, in a cloud of dust that still cloaked
her from head to foot, dragging down with her all the saints— both
male and female—she could name (Saint Chrysostom, Saint Luke,
Saint Paul), running all the words together in an outrageous mouthful of profanity that included the sacred vessels of the church as well
("*Tabernacle*, I'd sure like to get out of here!"). Language perceived
only through a prism of blasphemy whose rich colours, all gold and
incense, seemed to inspire her revolt and enliven her vivid truck-
driver's imagination.

"My child," said the Abbé, lifting his shoulders, "please watch your language."

But what did she care about him, a man in whom she saw only a little boy, a playmate she could bully by poking a bony fist in his face? (Since childhood she had only known her eight wicked and quarrelsome brothers, had been happier among lumberjacks than girls her own age, was proud and disdainful because within her, hidden beneath the bony exterior, burned an insatiable energy—the girl in her living apart or sometimes not at all, appearing only fleetingly on the features of the tough adolescent who swore and spat all the time. But it was this young girl, nevertheless, who had obtained in some obscure school the yellowed diploma she now pulled from her pocket with a satisfied smirk: "Schoolmistress. There, I told you so, didn't I?") "Jesus Christ, I'll talk how I like," she said, threatening the priest with her fist.

A flood of invective then poured over the pale face of Abbé Philippe: "I don't like priests, they bore me."

The Abbé finally resigned himself to listening in silence, eyes closed. Having rattled off with gusto her entire vocabulary of oaths, Judith was silent. After a moment she asked for the time and for information about the inspector of schools.

"I'm sorry," said the Abbé, "I don't know where he lives. I'm new here. I'm not even sure we have an inspector general."

Judith couldn't imagine a school without an inspector, and besides, in her village they had advised her to knock on his door to find lodging. (She showed the Abbé a letter signed by the mayor of Sainte-Félicie-du-bord, an illegible letter in which the Abbé pretended to take an interest.)

"You can come to my house," said the Abbé, blushing. "There is a little room and a kitchen, no fire in the room in the spring but it still isn't too cold."

Letting herself suddenly collapse on top of her suitcase, legs stretched out in front of her, arms crossed, Judith Prunelle explained, her voice breaking like a young boy's, that she didn't need anyone, that she could very well find her own lodging. Snatching off her beret with a rough gesture, she started scratching her head.

"Well, what are you hanging around staring at me like that for?"

"I was resting," said the Abbé awkwardly. "I just came from catechism. But I'm on my way now. It's confession today. . . ."

Before climbing on his bicycle he seemed to hesitate a moment, then, all in a rush, he said to Judith—who was still watching him with a surly air—"Perhaps we can work an exchange. You find me some pupils for catechism and I'll give you a roof over your head and some grammar lessons."

"Don't need grammar," said Judith Prunelle. "Don't need you either."

"Mathematics, perhaps?"

"I know my sums," said Judith Prunelle. "Don't need you!"

"Oh! Well, fine," said the Abbé, "if that's how you feel."

The Abbé set off toward the woods. Judith heard his anxious voice in the distance: "It will be dark soon. Better go back."

"Ain't afraid. Ain't afraid of the dark," she replied to no one in particular to fill the silence. But when she found herself alone on the road and could see only the black fields in front of her and the darkening sky above, when she heard the whispering of the leaves in the wind, she began to tremble, and sighed hopefully: "Now then, this here inspector, Jesus Christ, I've gotta find him."

And she set out again.

The school was closed. Judith Prunelle opened it. There was no sign of the inspector general. Judith decided to make a bed for herself on the bare floor of the schoolroom. "Jesus Christ, it's freezing," she groaned all night long, covering her head with her coat, her neck twisted against the suitcase she was using as a pillow. "Tomorrow as soon as it's daylight I'll have to light that goddam stove! Then I'll go find me some pupils. No pupils, no school. What use is a diploma anyway, I wonder? My father was right, the north's so empty, hell, who needs diplomas? I'll stuff a little history and geometry into their heads. I know all them dates by heart, you bet I do. I'm no moron like that goddam little priest thought. I'm smart; he'll see. Charles II the Bald, Charles the Fat, Charles III, Charles the Handsome, I've got them all at my fingertips, yessir, mister priest. And then there's Charles the Great too! You wouldn't believe it could get so cold, and me with no mitts. I've got a suitcase full of carrots. Holy Virgin, useful maybe, but not much help keeping warm. And then there's Charles IX and Charles X. I'll give them stupid goddam kids a beating and then we'll all eat carrots together. Holy smoke! I remember how all the boys in the village bawled like babies when they saw me leaving. And then they took off their caps. Jesus, that's respect for you! Maybe I should've gone back to the woods to cut trees, the sun's so warm there. Yeah, I used to drink a lot of beer there but I always stayed thin as a rake and the more I drank the thinner I got. And then there's Charles the Bold, they really oughta know that one. I'll hit them with the pointer if they don't get it. Well Jesus Christ, if it isn't the sun coming up; that's a surprise, eh? I'm sure glad to see it. I'll just shake myself up a little and eat a carrot and then bring in some wood. This is the life. Free as a bird, eh, and paid into the bargain. If only that goddam inspector general would get here."

Seated on her dusty desk, hair concealed under a large woollen beret, Judith ate a carrot. She was, to be precise, sitting on a part of the past of the School of Repentance, one of the school desks where Jean-Le-Maigre and Septième, in days gone by, had roughly carved their names with a knife and signed their amorous confessions with a black pencil *(Jean-Le-Maigre loves Martha the Hunchback—in life as in death. . .Septième begs Mademoiselle Lorgnette to wait for him after school. . .Dear Madame Casimir, would you be good enough to give me a match, you with your blouse bursting with treasure).* That fatal match was to be used to ignite a revolt and set fire to the school but this Judith Prunelle did not yet know. The new teacher swung her legs gently and happily welcomed the weak rays of sunlight that fell on her frozen knees. "Well by God, how about that for sunshine! Thank *you* St. Joseph. I was about ready to die of the cold in this place and wouldn't that've been cruel, by Jesus? Gotta put them through some of the Charlottes: Charlotte Elizabeth, Charlotte of Nassau, all that high society stuff. And I better get a rug for my school. They wipe their feet before they learn any history. I gotta teach the dirty little bastards some manners. Then I better clean up the goddam toilets. Its a real shame me arriving here like this without a word of welcome from the inspector general. I bet I know what's happened. They weren't expecting me because between times they've forgotten all about me coming. By Jonah, I'll teach them to remember with a few good clouts of the pointer. I'll show them."

It was six in the morning when Judith returned from the fields with her arms full of dry wood and children. From where they were sleeping in a damp, rat-infested barn, she had dragged a whole gang of kids seeking refuge for the night from a drunken grandfather, who was threatening to kill them. And from a wild-eyed mother, who was probably still wandering about as usual begging alms from the silent trees and a divine protection that the peaceful cloudless heavens could never grant her: "Alms for the love of God. My father's a drunk, my husband is sick, my children have no shoes."

"Mother was milking the cows one day," explained Josephine Poitiers, hanging on with one hand to the teacher's coat, "when suddenly, just like that, she went off her head and she's been like that ever since. It runs in the family, Grandpapa says," Josephine continued, walking along beside the teacher and her burden of children.

"Do you want me to fall, eh kid? Are you trying to knock me into the mud with all your goddam little brothers, eh?" But Josephine went right on pulling on Judith Prunelle's sleeve and trying with slow deliberation to explain:

"These things happen, Mademoiselle. It's a very great favour from God to have you in the school. We are certainly going to appreciate you. I had a vision yesterday in the barn. Our Lady told me you were coming."

"I don't understand a thing you're talking about," said Judith Prunelle in a sharp voice, and she abruptly deposited the children on the ground. "I'm not here to rescue orphans, for Christ's sake; I gotta look after my school."

"But she'll get better," said Josephine nodding wisely. Even though she had always been poor and had been frequently beaten by her grandfather ("Grandpapa loves us," she went on, taking hold of her little brothers' hands. "It's not his fault, it's just that when he's drunk he always wants to beat us up.") Josephine had none of the marks of a victim on her face: those profound scars that distinguish so easily the temporarily unfortunate of this world from those eternally doomed to wretchedness. She was, however, filthy from head to foot (the teacher could see the shadowy line of lice that separated the little girl's pigtails) but she wore her lack of cleanliness as if it were a handsome outift, and her delicate manner and large china eyes, which she opened wide to utter her solemn phrases, came as something of a surprise. The phrases seemed not just to come from some other world but from some other person.

"You act as if you thought you were some kind of fine lady, for Christ's sake! I'm not sure we're going to hit it off," said the teacher with rough impatience. "And anyway, I'm not sure I've got enough carrots for the whole family. What's his name, that one over there?" she asked, singling out the smallest of the little boys who was blowing his nose with his fingers. "He doesn't look too bright."

"His name is Chester," said Josephine very politely, "and he's off his head too but he was born that way, Grandpapa says. There are lots of idiots in the village, Mademoiselle; you just have to get used to it. But with us it runs in the family. Chester, don't blow your nose in front of Mademoiselle. She doesn't like it."

He can blow all he likes," said Judith Prunelle, "I'm no princess. You can see that easy enough."

Then flinging open the door of the school with a flourish, she cried out: "Well here it is, for Christ's sake! *My* school. And I'm gonna start teaching right away while it's still warm."

And Josephine, Chester, Marie-Ange Poitiers (and Hector Poitiers too) all seated themselves in a circle around Judith Prunelle and listened to her talk about one of her favourite subjects, the Creation of the World.

While Judith was creating the world, brandishing her thin fists at the blackboard, Chester Poitiers dreamed of his mother, wandering through the fields, the stones on the road tearing at her bare, bleeding feet that moved all alone on the white roadway. Josephine smiled and said every now and again into the ear of Chester or Hector, "Don't make so much noise with your nose, Mademoiselle doesn't like that."

Judith Prunelle interrupted her lesson to say shortly, "Jesus Christ, a nose doesn't bother me. Make whatever noise you want, Chester. I don't even hear it."

Josephine rose from her seat to explain. Mademoiselle asked her to sit down and the lesson continued. Chester closed his eyes.

"Just imagine, there wasn't a monkey, a mushroom, a drop of rain! I bet you can't imagine that, eh? Well there was nothing, everywhere. Not an ant, not even a caterpillar."

"And God created the world in seven days," said Josephine "and on the seventh day he rested. Monsieur le Curé Lacloche told me. Our Lady told me too. She talked to me yesterday. She was standing on the manure pile. She was very beautiful. She had golden hair. And she said, 'Josephine, would you like to boil some milk for my baby who is thirsty?' I ran to the house. There wasn't any milk left. When I came back, Our Lady wasn't there any more."

"Will you sit *down?*" said Judith Prunelle, knocking Josephine off her seat. This isn't a classroom it's a pigsty!"

"I saw her four times in the barn," said Josephine. "She promised to come back. She said to me: 'Josephine, you're going to be very unhappy. If I were you, I would hide my bread under the mattress every night. Because there's going to be a famine in the village. In the meantime, say your prayers.' "

"And there was no smoke and no fire in those days," continued Judith Prunelle passionately. "There was nothing. Then suddenly, it all began, all by itself, like someone starting to laugh in the night. The brooks, the seas, the rivers, everything began to bubble, like anger inside you, like soup boiling over the pot. My children it was a beautiful sight to see."

"The lion lay down with the lamb," interrupted Josephine, "and the wolf in the arms of the deer. Our Lady shed many tears. I should tell you, Mademoiselle, that my little brothers don't wash very often. But there are lots of people don't wash, my grandfather says. Then I asked Our Lady what her name was. She said: 'Josephine, I am called Notre-Dame-Des-Petits-Sous.' "

Marie-Ange and Hector were asleep in their seats. Chester, whose square head stood out above the others, seemed to be meditating under the protective umbrella of his long eyelashes. While the teacher's conversation abounded in rippling images and seas overflowing their banks, saliva flowed from Chester's mouth copiously, soaking the collar of his shirt.

"It's nothing, Mademoiselle, he slobbers. It runs in the family."

"It runs in the family," Chester seemed to be saying, shaking his head.

But since Josephine talked so tirelessly and with such measured wisdom, her brothers, already encouraged by mental laziness, never opened their mouths unless to say with profound amazement— "Oh, Josephine!"—and even that rarely. Eventually they said nothing at all. As for poor Chester, he slobbered more and more, justifying Our Lady's prophecy to Josephine: 'Josephine, your brother Chester has a pretty big head for his age. He'll end badly. He will be the village idiot. I hope you don't mind too much.' So then Josephine said to Our Lady: 'You're lucky, you are, that your baby doesn't have a big head like Chester's.'

"And the fish danced," said the teacher, "and then the birds with their paper-thin wings flew all around in the springtime and there were giraffes walking very quietly on the new grass making no noise, no noise at all."

"Was there a sky up above?" Josephine stood up to ask the question. "Was God up there seated on a throne of clouds?"

"Yes, he was," she replied, answering her own question, all-knowing. "He was there and he said, 'My beloved mountains, my beloved hills.'"

"Go to the toilet," shouted Judith Prunelle, pushing Chester toward the door. "If that isn't shameful, first day in my class and during the Creation of the World too, right in the middle of the storms and lightning!"

"These things happen, Mademoiselle," said Josephine, wiping up an incriminating puddle under the seat. "I should tell you it happens to him often, Mademoiselle, but I've always got a pocketful of handkerchiefs."

Josephine was still chattering like a mountain stream when Abbé Philippe appeared on the doorstep of the classroom, a woollen blanket under his arm, gazing at Judith with eyes dulled by lack of sleep.

"My child," he said, in a tone almost sinister, "I have just administered the last rites to poor Horace. He breathed his last in my arms."

Not knowing what to reply Judith made a face indicating her disgust, then said coldly:

"Well now, M'sieur le Curé: me, I don't know this Horace of yours and anyway everybody's dying these days for Christ's sake! We've all got to go, me and you too, eh? It's not my fault if he's dead, this fellow.

"A moment of silence," begged Abbé Philippe, pressing his hands to his head. "Just a brief moment, please. . . ."

"And anyway, is that all you've got to say to me about my school? Me expecting all kinds of congratulations. Well, lemme tell you I'm disappointed. I really am."

"I *do* congratulate you," said the Abbé. "It's admirable. Especially at seven o'clock in the morning. I apologize for bothering you in class, but I thought you might be cold and . . ."

Judith snatched the woollen blanket from the Abbé, murmuring a quick thank you and adding immediately, "You could have thought to bring us a little bread. These dirty little kids have to eat, y'know. Sit *down* everybody," she roared at the children who had stood up to greet the priest. "I don't want no ceremonies for a priest!"

Josephine alone remained standing.

"I am Josephine Poitiers," she said with authority. "It's a very great favour from God to have you in our parish, Monsieur l'Abbé. We are certainly going to appreciate you. The village has been very sad since Monsieur le Curé Lacloche left. Everybody is crying. But everybody's happy too, Grandpapa says. These are Chester, Marie-Ange and Hector Poitiers. They weren't with me in the barn when I saw Our Lady all dressed in red, holding her baby in her arms."

"Our Lady?" the Abbé asked in surprise.

"Of course," said Josephine. "Our Lady of the Blueberries. She sat down right beside me on the straw. We ate blueberries."

"We'll talk about all that again some time," said the Abbé calmly. "Do you know your prayers? Did your little brothers learn their catechism with Monsieur le Curé Lacloche?"

"I taught them their lessons," said Jospehine, "I taught Monsieur le Curé Lacloche too when he came to our house to drink with Grandpapa Poilu. But Grandpapa told me not to talk to you because you don't drink."

"All right then," said the Abbé, "let's stop talking."

But Josephine went on chirping like a bird on a branch.

"I would like very much to confess," she said. "I know all the others' sins (Chester, wipe your nose; Monsieur l'Abbé doesn't like that). I met our Lady of the Green Peas in the field the other day (Chester your nose!). She had lost her bowl. She said to me: 'Josephine, you ought to found a convent, right here among the peas and the radishes and gather around you all the village idiots to teach them God's law.' And then I saw fire in the sky. Our Lady said to me: 'Don't be afraid, Josephine, it's the dragon of faith coming down on your house. If I were you I'd go to the kitchen and see if your Grandfather's breath is on fire.' I ran into the house. Grandpapa had drunk a whole bottle of whisky. To put him to sleep, I told him the story of St. Gondrian. 'Ah, Saint Gondrian,' said Grandpapa. 'Of course! I know that one. How is he? By the way, Josephine, where is your mother? She's getting so big,' Grandpapa said, 'what's to become of us all? If I wasn't so drunk I'd go look for her.' I took Grandpapa's hand and I said, 'Let's go look for mother. Our Lady will tell me where she is. Our Lady tells me everything.' Grandpapa cried and said, 'These days the saints don't give you anything. In the old days your St. Gondrian used to put a bottle of whisky under my pillow every morning.' I said to him, 'Walk straight, Grandpapa. What will Mama think if she sees you like that?'

"'I've got a gun,' said Grandpapa. 'I can blow all your heads off and then—silence. I can drink in peace. There are too many children in this world. I'd like to sleep forever. Snore with happiness.' (Grandpapa was crying a lot, he was so sorry for having killed his dear little

Josephine.) 'Hey, there she is, there's your mother,' said Grandpapa, wiping away his tears to see her better. 'Come to me, Rose. I open my arms, my house, my heart to you. What's the matter, Rose? You look so strange. Where did you cut your feet like that?'

"'My dear little Josephine,' Mother said, sitting in the middle of the road. 'Have you looked after the cow? Have you boiled the milk for the baby?' I should tell you, Monsieur le Curé, that when we got to the house we wiped up the blood that dripped from Mother's feet and put her to bed. But suddenly Grandpapa got all black with anger and took the gun down off the wall.

"'And Chester, where's Chester? I'm going to kill that kid,' he said.

"Chester, Chester," Josephine moaned, crying suddenly in the middle of her story, to the dismay of Abbé Philippe and Judith Prunelle who were watching her. "Poor Chester. Grandpapa filled his body full of holes."

Seeing himself dead, Chester began to cry and all the Poitiers children imitated him noisily, so that Judith had to give two loud raps with the pointer on the blackboard to command silence.

"Jesus Christ," she cried. "What have I got myself into? You, mister priest, can you tell me what we're ever gonna do, you and me, with this here school?"

Abbé Philippe shrugged his shoulders and did not reply.

Réjean Ducharme
The Wedding Gown

Little more is known of Réjean Ducharme today than he revealed in 1966 in an autobiographical note on the fly-leaf of his most famous novel, *L'Avalée des avalés* (translated by Barbara Bray in 1968 as *The Swallower Swallowed*). He then wrote that he had been born (only once, in 1942) at St-Félix-de-Valois, that he was not dead yet, nor married, but that had he wived to suit his fancy he would by now have fathered 5,768 children. Four novels and several plays later he is still one of the most mysterious figures on the Quebec literary scene. He has never appeared in public or released a photograph of himself, yet he is acknowledged both at home and in France to be one of the most original writers of his generation and he has had a strong influence on young Quebec novelists and playwrights.

Although Ducharme has published no short stories it would be a mistake to exclude him from a book like this that groups all the important writers of the sixties, so as a representative sample of his fiction I have chosen a passage from his second, as yet untranslated novel, *Le Nez qui voque* (1967).

Mille Milles, the sixteen-year-old narrator, and his girl friend Chateaugué, fourteen, are refugees from childhood cast away in contemporary Montreal. They have adopted a communal name, Tate, and have sworn to commit suicide (which they refer to euphemistically as "clearing the decks") rather than succumb to adulthood, to the world and the flesh. But while Chateaugué is for Mille Milles the symbol of innocence and purity, he finds that she stirs up strong contradictory currents in him, as revealed in the passage that follows.

William Kinsley is a specialist in Barth, Pynchon and Nabakov so he is well equipped to translate the verbal aerobatics of Réjean Ducharme. He is also author of many pieces on satire and Professor of Eighteenth-Century English Literature at l'Université de Montréal.

The Wedding Gown

Talking pessimistically is pleasant. If we were talking pessimistically it wasn't because we were convinced by what we were saying, but because black ideas, like black tulips, are the most beautiful. As we kept walking the sidewalks and talking gloom to each other, something happened which couldn't fail to have consequences, consequences that would occur before we cleared the decks. We were passing by a *haute couture* shop window, and Chateaugué recalled the vow I had made to buy her the most beautiful dress in the world. She stopped in front of the luxuriant display, and planted herself there, fastened herself there. She didn't want to budge.

"That's the one!" she cried. "How beautiful! That's the one I want."

Hands glued to the window like limpets, face flattened against the glass wall, she was experiencing frightful joy, frightening desires. She told me to come over.

"Come here. Closer. Come and see. Come on! Look—that one, there! That's the one, at the end of my finger, that I want to die in."

It was a white dress stitched with stars, a moonlight dress that flowed out from the waist. A dress for a true woman, a woman who hides her feet under her dress, a woman who walks within it secretly.

"You're right out of your mind! That's a wedding gown."

"Sure it's a wedding gown, but that doesn't make any difference. I like it anyway. If you want to buy a dress for me, buy me that one. I've never asked you for anything else."

The wide window bellied inward under the pressure of Chateaugué's covetousness.

"You'll have it. We'll come and steal it."

"When?"

"Tonight."

We played detective. We circled the block. We combed the walls of the five-storey building to see if there was a way of breaking and entering by night. At the back, along a macabre blind alley, we found what we were looking for: a cellar window with a grating held in place by only a few screws.

The grating is only held on by screws. The robbery is set for tonight, not long from now. So it's tonight, this very night, that the consequences of what happened this afternoon will occur. We're waiting for the middle of the night to start out. We, Tate, are cold now; it's cold in our room. Chateaugué is so cold that she has to massage her legs to keep from freezing.

"It's ugly, skin is," she says, rubbing her legs. "It's like poorly made porcelain, not baked enough. It's like dead. It's flabby. It's nothing. It's like paper. You look at it and it doesn't say anything to you."

I look at that skin that doesn't say anything to her, skin that I hear playing the violin. I gather up all my courage. I've had a question to ask Chateaugué ever since we left the restaurant. Whatever happens, I must ask her. At the restaurant we, Tate, were inadvertently seated within earshot of a quartet of horny adolescent schoolboys. They were talking dirty and Chateaugué heard everything they said. She was even listening, ears pricked up, laughing. Besides, I think it was for her benefit that they were talking dirty.

"You know what the Indians call a bra? A tit-rack!"

"I know a girl that has such big ones she has to wear a hammock."

"That's nothing compared to the one that has to buy two parachutes every time because she can't find anything big enough in one piece."

Chateaugué had listened, roaring with laughter, hardly blushing, leaning over to hear better.

I've screwed up all the courage I need.

"Tate, for the first time in our life I want to ask you an embarrassing question. Can I?"

"It's all right with me. I don't believe you."

She seems very much intrigued, but at the same time she's getting ready to have a trick played on her. She holds herself up straight, ready for anything, even the impossible: a revelation.

"Tate, Chateaugue, do you realize . . . that . . . that you have breasts?"

"That I have what?" she exclaims.

She doesn't understand, not at all. She doesn't have any idea what I'm getting at. She has the impression, since the question was supposed to be embarrassing, that I'm talking about pimples. She tries to look at her own face by lowering her eyes.

"Where?"

"You don't know what they are? I mean . . . those . . ." Gesturing as I speak, I point to her sheltered little breasts with the end of my finger. Her face suddenly relaxes and lights up.

"Those? Why sure! What an idea! I have them, you have them, everybody has them. Why shouldn't I realize it?"

She seems relieved that that's all it is. She was a little afraid.

"Me? I don't have them. I'm not like you, I'm not a woman!" I said that cynically, in an outraged voice, strong in the prerogatives of my flat chest.

Chateaugué's face darkens again.

"What do you mean? You do too have them. They aren't like mine, but you have them. Mine are all swelled up like a pig's; yours are tiny like a cat's. But they're the same thing. They're in the same place, so they're the same thing, right?"

"Aw, forget it."

She comes back to it, insistently; her curiosity has been piqued. She probes to find out what I have at the back of my mind. She senses that I'm hiding something from her, that something is going on behind her back. The silly argument excites me so bestially I can't see clearly any more. I want so much to kiss her! She's seeking, waiting, wanting, offering herself. She holds her hand out to me so I can help her climb down into hell. All I'd have to do is pluck her, hold out my hand, and she'd fall to the bottom of the depths from which I'm looking up at her. I want so much to kiss her little breasts that my ears are roaring and it seems as if my lips have already made contact with the red cotton of the blouse that hides those little breasts. Discouraged by the violence of my sensuality, I suddenly let my big head fall and hang against my chest. Chateaugué keeps on talking, but I've stopped listening. Let her talk! Let her go on talking forever! Let her go to the devil with her innocence. Let her spout it forever, that innocence so intent on self-improvement, so eager to change into atrocities, that innocence in such a hurry to change into filth. She has grabbed a handful of my hair and is shaking my head tenderly, awkwardly, hesitantly.

"Mille Milles. Mille Milles? You're all red! Do you feel sick? Are you sick, Mille Milles? Do you want to throw up? Answer me. Answer me!"

"Ivugivic!"*

She is standing in front of me. I can feel her face hanging over me, suspended above me like a threat. Right in front of my eyes I have her skirt, with her belly behind it, her belly living behind it, her belly warm behind it. Heedless of everything, I suddenly let my heavy head lean against this belly, sink into the warmth of this belly, and I leave it there, I leave it there to rest. Chateaugué brings her other hand up to join the one already on my head. Now all her hands are moving on my head, or almost aren't moving on my head.

"What's the matter, Mille Milles? Are you hurt? What's the matter? Tell Chateaugué."

She speaks with a catch in her throat. She's afraid of me. Women are afraid of men who lose control of themselves. They're afraid when men get frightened. I seize Chateaugué by the wrists and squeeze, to hurt her, to make her suffer.

"I'll tell you what the matter is! You disgust me! You're not pure, you're just ignorant. You're not chaste, you're stupid. You're only a bloody woman! You're in a big hurry to know how a woman works, eh? You can't wait, eh? It's tough to be a woman, to have all that dirty machinery and not know how to use it, eh? You never *wanted* to be pure, eh? If you *were* pure it wasn't on purpose, eh? You're completely innocent, eh? Grinning from ear to ear whatever happens, eh? You're ready for anything; all you need is for somebody to tell you how to go about it, eh? The first comer, that's what's in store for you. You'll think it's good. You'll think it's funny just like all the others. You'll laugh from ear to ear. You're only a bloody woman, Chateague, that's what's the matter! That's what makes me sick."

The idea of evil has never come into her head. What a bloody simpleton! Suddenly I hear someone talking. Suddenly her voice is sombre and grave.

"You mustn't say everything, Tate. You mustn't say everything. Keep your secrets, Tate. Keep yourself to yourself. Don't force things. Don't cause pain."

I feel queer all over. I know what's got hold of me. At the beginning, at the very beginning when I conceived the idea of Chat-

*Chateaugué's Eskimo name.

eaugué's purity, I also conceived the idea of her impurity. The more I love her purity, the more I love her impurity. I have chosen the purity, the purity of Chateaugué, the purity of our friendship. But the idea of Chateaugué's impurity keeps asserting itself, trying to force its way into existence. The stronger one idea is, the stronger the opposite. What a lot of words! What a lot of words! What a lot of air! What a lot of water! Chateaugué, I'm a monster, an inveterate dastardurbater, zealously obsessed with sex. If I let myself go I wouldn't stop at caressing Chateaugué. By this time we'd be dead of debauchery. We'd be dead and buried, both of us. All of Tate, all of us would belong to the Plutonian kingdom. That's all she's waiting for, the little whore. I can't wait to die. If I don't leave right away, it will be too late, and I'll look completely ridiculous when I go. I still have a little dignity left. If I keep on waiting I'll lose that. Why this delay before clearing the decks? For whom?

I know why, at bottom. I'm waiting till our friendship has won out, has escaped shining bright from the swamp it's been shoved into; till it stands shining bright on the summit of the white mountain, whiter than the snow of the summit. I'm waiting till our friendship has lost, till it lies defeated in the slimy muddy water, till the green swamp-flies have finished eating its rotted flesh. It's the law of contraries. I have nothing left but our friendship, and I'm waiting till I've committed the commonplace act that will ruin it. I want to die and I want to live. I want to live! I've never wanted to live so much as I have since it's been necessary for me to clear the decks. The desire I feel to take this whole disgusting world into my arms is as strong as the desire to take Chateaugué into my arms. My desire to conquer everything is as strong as my desire to lose everything.

Enough Tate! O you who bring all to pass, please me, let me be nothing but putrefaction and stink. O you who bring all to pass, make me like the corpse of the cat that floats on the slimy water. O you who bring all to pass, make me want to vomit when I look at myself in Chateaugué's face! O you who bring all to pass, change my skin to bronze, swell my chest with light, transform my lukewarmness to ice, make me worthy of myself. Bloody bestialities!

If we must call a spade a spade, the verb love must give over to wanttodofilthythingswithyou. Let's conjugate that, the verb wanttodofilthythingswithyou. I wanttodofilthythingswithyou, you wantmetodobeastlythingswithyou, we wanttododisgustingthings-together. I love Chateaugué. If I love Chateaugué, I wanttodofilthythingswithher. I don't even have to force myself to admit that I'm disgusting. I'm naturally disgusting. I need to force myself to admit that I'm not disgusting. I love you. You love me. We love each other. We sleep together and we don't do anything bad, but I have to force myself. Sometimes, before we fall asleep, we talk to each other, smoking face to face as if all we had was faces, blowing smoke into each other's face, as if only our wings were jostling together under the covers, as if we were angels. But I have to force myself. To stay pure you need force; you need to force yourself. You need courage; you need to encourage yourself. The most tempting thing about chastity is the courage you need to preserve it. If I'm chaste it's because I've been strong; if I'm strong I'm worthy of myself. I have a right to be proud of myself and climb up onto any pedestal.

"Shall we go?"

"Where?"

"To get my dress. It's two o'clock. It's dark enough, it's dark dark. No one will see us stealing at this hour. You can't even see your hand in front of your face."

"The dress? Oh yes, that's right. I'd forgotten. Let's get going, Boeing."

We aren't going to go skipping across Montreal on foot with a stolen wedding gown under our arm. We decide to take a taxi and hail one that's cruising by, like in a murder mystery. We ask the cabdriver if he has a screwdriver. There's one in the glove compartment. We ask him if he'll lend it to us. He'll lend it to us. We ask him to park at the entrance of the blind alley so as to cover us, and to wait there for us. He says okay.

We plunge into the thick shadows of the alley, which seems like a mountain pass. We plunge in with the screwdriver, thinking of Napoleon crossing the pass of Mont-Cenis. The dark buildings along the alley rise right up into the vault of night. We seem to be at the bottom of an abyss, at the bottom of those structures that stand almost touching, bathing in the volatile black liquid of the night.

The four screws that screw the grating that secures the window are quickly unscrewed. Chateaugué shatters the glass of the window with a kick. Feet first, I work my way between jaws with glass teeth, and jump. It's a long way down; I didn't expect it to be nearly so long. I fall onto a surface cluttered with broken furniture and crack my skull on something. I get up and call Chateaugué. I'm bleeding and in bad shape, but that doesn't bother me. A splinter of glass has pierced my cheek. With a shudder I yank it out. Without seeing me Chateaugué follows, and I go ahead of her without seeing where I put my feet. To get to the show window we have to keep advancing in the direction we're advancing in. I advance. I break down the doors we run into on the way. I find it pleasant to break down doors; it eases the heart. If I didn't have any doors to break down, my heart would explode like a bomb. Chateaugué follows me silently, upsetting everything along the way, touching me to make sure I'm always there ahead of her. She is the cause of the rage that burns in my heart.

The show window is lit up as bright as day. Tate, hidden together silently behind a muslin screen, watches the rare automobiles and the last passersby pass by. Tate holds each other by the hand before crossing the Rubicon. Tate looks each other in the eye and feels sure that after such a burglary there will be no place for Tate in society. We're afraid all of a sudden; we're on the brink of robbery. If we change our mind, our friendship was only a game; if we steal, it wasn't a game: we'd have to clear the decks or go to prison. Will our courage fail us? Are we going to give up at the first real test? Are we going to be terrified and return empty-handed? We won't let ourselves betray Tate. Tate steels ourself to steal.

"Tate, why aren't you a girl like me? Why don't you wear a dress the way I do?"

There's Chateaugué beginning to have ideas. The robbery won't amount to anything. The roots of our friendship are all eaten away by ideas. After examining the situation, we work out a plan. We won't just take away the dress, we'll take the dummy too. We're not going to start undressing the dummy under the eyes of the rare automobiles and the last passersby.

Time passes. The taxi waits. The ten or eleven dummies stand upright on a sort of common pedestal. Well out of sight behind this platform, we crawl along to within reach of the dummy we want to attack and kidnap. We grab her by a foot, turn her upside down and catch her in our arms so she won't get too badly smashed. Then we take off with her, laughing with fear, fleeing on hands and knees. Since the object of our covetousness holds her arms outstretched, she doesn't fit through the opening of the cellar window. We try in vain to think of a way to get her out without amputating. Don't want to ampue Tate. Suddenly there's a haggard head at the window, the cabdriver. I get a spurt of inspiration.

"There's a big tip for you if you don't talk. Take this dummy by the head and pull. We've got to make it or break it. Hey, take it easy! That's not a sack of flour, it's damasked brocade. Hey, don't sweep the street with her! Pick her up and carry her in your arms. She won't bite."

I could go on shouting insults at the driver all night, I'm so mad. At Chateaugué, too. A girl! I should wear a dress! She wishes I was a girl like her! The driver holds the dummy by the head and Chateaugué holds it by the feet. I open the door of the taxi for them. They set it down carefully on the back seat, as if it were a baby. The driver is a real cool cat, singing all the way home. He sings *Mon Pantalon est décousu* to the tune of Rocky Mendelssohn's wedding march.

I give him ten dollars for a tip. His face changes. He looks at my tattered ten-dollar bill as if he wanted to vomit on it. He doesn't think it's enough, and lets us know it. And I bled myself white to please him! He almost runs us down as he leaves, peeling off like a rocket, spinning his rear wheels at top speed and shooting gravel at us. Let him go turn us in! Let him do it, the dirty old wet blanket.

The bride has her forehead torn off and her nose broken; she's missing an arm on one side and three fingers on the other. That's all. She's no worse for wear than that. We don't know where to put her. We put her at the head of our bed, so she can watch us sleep. We put her in place of the orange crate that used to serve as our wall-to-wall bookcase. Her head touches the ceiling, which slopes with the pitch of the roof. We contemplate this calm intruder. We turn our backs on her, then whip around suddenly to surprise her. But she surprises us. We're just not used to having a dummy in our room, a stolen dummy at that. To domesticate it, Chateaugué baptizes it. She smears its face with ink, as she did with the ugly little statue but taking great care not to spatter the dress. The dress isn't as dirty as it might be. But it's not as clean as it was. It has some tears too.

"We have two sculptures now, Tate—Bride and Ugly. Here's Bride, who's dead in a living dress, and here's Ugly, who's dead in a dead dress."

"You mean, false in a true dress and false in a false dress."

"No."

The robbery is over. She has her dress. I can breathe. Our friendship, after so many millions of words, has finally made a move, has finally begun to take shape. The day is over, too, since we're sleepy and will have to wait till we've slept to live a little more. Worn out, Tate lies down, side by side. We fall asleep instantly. Our legs interlocked, our eyes closed, looking at each other through our eyelids, we sleep. We look like two angels. Our wings rumple each other under the covers. Tomorrow, in the sun, like flowers, our wings will unrumple. Suddenly, living is so sweet. Suddenly, living is so bitter.

André Major

The Thief of Bonsecours Market

André Major (b. 1942) with the two following authors, Jacques Renaud (1943) and Claude Jasmin (1930), represents the *"joual"* school of Quebec writing. Taking their language and experience from the streets, shops, and factories of the big city (mainly Montreal) they depict, each in his own style, the lives and trials of the rough, politically committed, urban poor.

André Major began as a poet, turned novelist with *Le Cabochon* (1964), *La Chair de poule* (1965), and *Le Vent du Diable* (1968), was one of the founders of the separatist review and publishing house *Partis Pris*, has earned his living as a literary critic on *Le Devoir*, as a free-lance journalist, and now works for Radio-Canada. The story collected here is taken from *La Chair de poule* and shows the fashionable tourist quarter, "Le Vieux Montréal", when it was Montreal's Cabbagetown. André Major captures it with something of the same bitter intensity and gritty humour as Hugh Garner uses in writing about Toronto.

Patricia Claxton is a professional translator who teaches at l'Université de Montréal. She has translated historian Marcel Trudel's *The Beginnings of New France* (1973), his *Atlas of New France* (1969), parts of the B & B Commission and the Le Dain Reports, and an article by Pierre Elliott Trudeau.

The Thief of Bonsecours Market

Grandpapa Lafortune stood in the middle of the market place and waved his arms. He had the undivided if desultory attention of all the housewives and idlers within earshot.

That morning Bonsecours Market exuded as pungent a smell of vegetables as it ever did. Like as not because the tubers, shrivelled and shrunken by the frost, had begun to thaw and rot with the early arrival of spring. Grandpapa was bellyaching because the cabbages for sale weren't to his liking. "Cabbages ain't what they used to be," he kept proclaiming with relish to all and sundry.

It was true, too. Those big, juicy, old-fashioned cabbages just weren't to be had any more. They were fresh-cut, what you could find nowadays at the market, but nothing like the ones Grandpapa sold when he was in business a good twenty years before.

In the struggling April sunlight the old man's face, for all its mischievousness, had a deathly purplish cast. When he went through his antics every morning, what he was doing was turning back the clock, fending off the shadow of death that he could see descending as relentlessly as the cabbages wilting in the sun. He capered about, insect-like, his battered old cap askew on his bald, greasy head. His pipe, gripped in his sand-dry lips, seemed as much a part of him as his nose, his ears, and his constant stench of negligent old age. "What good'll working do me," he would say with a rattle of phlegm in his throat, "The Good Lord'll come for me pretty soon anyhow." Then he would shiver, frown, and retreat to his memories of other days.

"Cabbages ain't nothing but a sham," he hollered that Monday morning that changed my life. "Just look at that! No bigger'n a mekkintosh!"

His sandpapery hand bobbed up and down, cradling the degenerate vegetable, the target of all the contempt he could muster with what life was left in him. What little life. . . . There was a saying he often thought about, as brutal as a fist before your nose: "You were born of dust, my friend, and to dust you will return." His future he imagined as a weightless pile of ashes scattering every which way in the wind. "Sad, sad," he would mutter to himself.

But now, goaded on by the defiant if watery glint in the old man's eye, the vendor became instinctively defensive about his merchandise.

"Look here, Pop, if you don't like 'em, go back for your cabbages to Laprairie where you came from. Maybe they'll be bigger'n better'n mine. This ain't '14 no more, you know, it's the age of machines and you better get that straight in your head. It's gotta be my fault if things don't grow like they did?"

Right in step with the march of progress, he thought he was, preaching like that at a broken-down old man with one foot in the grave. But he was so busy shooting off his mouth like a fishwife that he didn't see Grandpapa filching his cabbages and stuffing them into the copious pockets of his ratty old overcoat. When he had taken what he wanted, the old man cavorted indignantly around and his voice rose to a screech.

"Shut your yap, blockhead! I know more about it than you'll ever know, 'cause I can see further'n the end of my nose, you hear me?"

Then briskly, wispy as a cornstalk, he turned his back and left, casting a baleful glare at the passers-by about him and dragging his left leg back to his cantankerous solitude.

The market-place returned to normal, slow-moving and smelly as before.

I'd seen Grandpapa Lafortune swiping those cabbages. Couldn't miss it from where I was, and it gave me a great idea. I could swipe apples the same way. I'd worked up quite an appetite prowling around. Hungry business, sinfulness, especially playing hooky. I really wanted some apples, big, red, juicy mackintoshes, so good you can't forget them once you've tasted them. I'd just turned twelve and I had my own secret life and was proud of it. No one ever knew what

I was doing, adults were so dumb and stupidly hung up on all their thankless chores. Their children were rowdy enough now, but sooner or later they'd inherit those chores too. Children change around Bonsecours Market, just like cabbages. Time and their parents' example make them mean and thick in the head. That's the way life goes. Might as well get used to it. Why bellyache if it doesn't get you anywhere? The little people soon learn that their place in life is to feed their families and give them a little ambition. Not too much, mind you. That would be sinful, and beyond them anyway. Just a bit, so they can live through hardship. That's enough for the chicken-hearted little souls in my neighbourhood. Already my immature grey matter had registered these things and I'd made up my mind to fight them. I wanted nothing to do with poverty like Grandpapa Lafortune's, having to swipe things at his age after toiling all his barren, bitter life. I'd swipe things right now and make a future for myself, far away from the clamour of the city and its bodily exhaustion. I dreamed of fields and silvery mountains, fresh air and oranges. It was all fantasy, comic-strip stuff, because the back lane and the market-place were as close as I'd ever come to paradise.

I was terribly afraid of what the future might bring. The thought of living like an insect, like the rest, poor and niggardly, captive of a factory, stoop-shouldered by thirty, with nothing in my heart but a clammy fear of hunger and of dying all alone or surrounded by a clutch of bawling, brat-faced children. . . . That was my nightmare. My conception of society. It haunted me and kept me awake, going round and round in my brain. My brain; I used to wonder what it might be good for. Still do.

Once in a while, as on that morning, I fled from school and wandered restlessly about the neighbourhood, avidly taking in whatever sights my birthright and my family's condition could offer, seeing what kind of life I'd be leading in a few years and doubtless being turned off it for good. And so I had this real and unvarnished conception of life, of a ruthless struggle to be escaped only if one knew what was what. And the market-place was where I learned the best of my out-of-school lessons. There the struggle was clear-cut and neatly reduced to three activities: purchase, sale and theft. Life in a nutshell.

But Grandpapa's case was always beyond my understanding. Was it a gift or a knack he'd learned? I might not have his gift, and learning the art of theft would take time. Should I chance it? Just to see?

Intention is all very well, but you've got to have the guts to go through with it. Not everyone's got guts.

It was fear that finally sent me after those apples. Yes, fear of maybe never having the guts. I stuck my hand in the pile of apples and what I got was a boot in the ass. The row there was! Ranting and raving, on and on, and clouts on the back of my head. Plus the feast the gossips had at my expense.

"Imagine . . .! Just a child and a thief already"!

The tongues wagged on, saying atrocious things about me, accusing me of all kinds of crimes, already picturing me dangling from the end of a rope.

Learning from life, that was. Yes sir! Later on there'd be more of the same, only worse, because I wouldn't have my tender age for an excuse. Crestfallen, I returned to my little back lane, my refuge, knowing I'd committed my first adult sin and was older and wiser for it. From that day on I felt a bit superior to the other kids.

Before going home that evening, I was feeling pretty lonesome and I went to see Grandpapa Lafortune. I told him the tale of my misadventure in such a babble that he was soon pretty worried.

"A lot of hogwash!" he barked. "You got a screw loose or something? What you getting at?"

I hesitated to tell him that it was because of him, thanks to him, that I'd dared violate the laws of ownership. Would he be flattered that I'd followed his example? Or what? You never know with old people. They turn like weathercocks.

"I saw you . . . the cabbages. . . ."

Oh, how I made him dance with rage and indignation at that, and on one leg too, the right one.

"Goodgawdamighty! You better learn a thing or two, you little varmint! I'm not a thief. I got a right to them there cabbages. Who was it had the vegetable business in the first place? Me, that's who and nobody else, and I ran it a lot better than Albert, that fathead. Why should I cough up for cabbages? Ungrateful bastard, Albert. It's because of me his business works. I got his customers for him, and long before he was born, too. Folks today don't show no thanks for the good done 'em."

So he was lying too, just like the rest. Seeing him go on like that over the idea I'd got of him made me pretty sad. He didn't have enough guts or pride to admit what he really was. Quite a revelation, people's gutlessness. So they were all the same, were they? Tiresome, petty, gutless little creatures worth even less than their miserable pilferings.

"Grandpapa Lafortune, you're not worth a cabbage, not even one the size of a mekkintosh"! And I left his hovel with an air of finality and disgust, as though I'd never come back. I never saw him alive again. On the afternoon of the next day, since it was pouring rain and his window was open, his neighbour, fat Mathilde, went to see what was up. She found Grandpapa flopped over his cabbages, his teeth clenched on his pipestem and his body doubled over as though with stomach cramp.

"The Good Lord has punished him," thought I, my grey matter now slightly less immature. "He shouldn't have lied to me. It brings bad luck."

Life in the market-place went on, but not the way it had before with Grandpapa hopping on his right leg and his mouth all twisted, shouting curses and insults. The market's just not the same. Like a graveyard now. When I go there, people recognize me and they're afraid of me. I'm a terror to them. I get booted off, all right, but I don't often come home with empty pockets. My reputation is made. I'm the black sheep of the neighbourhood. Is it my fault if my vice isn't discreet like Grandpapa's was?

Uncles and aunts have stopped asking me what I'm going to be some day because I'd always tell them the biggest thief in the country. Pa knocks my head around a lot, but I've got a hard one and they won't get me that way. Ma buys candles and lights them so I'll be cured. I think it's a shame to waste money like that because I won't ever be good. I've seen what life's like and I'll never be good again. I know if I stop stealing I'll be just like everyone else; I'll be had by the rich, the bosses who work you till you sweat like an animal. I won't sweat to make the rich fat.

You've got to look after yourself in this life.

Pa's still got no job. He thinks its great for the rest of us. It'd do us more good if he stole, then we'd eat like other people. He ought to do like me, not beat me when I bring home food. He's afraid of the police. Got no guts.

I ask Ma why it's so warm in springtime.

"Don't ask questions," she snaps.

Leaning hard on the roller she presses out the dough till it's thin, thin.

"I do love apple pie, Ma."

"You won't get none if you keep on at me."

All the houses are damp around here. The walls sweat winter or summer. Everything seems sticky. You never know whether it's hot or cold. Not hot, not cold, but in between. Shivery. Shiver-shiver. I wonder why our houses are all stuck together like they'd fall over if they weren't. Because of wind and storms maybe? I won't ever know. Better think about something else.

Think about the lane. I still love it there. Had fun with the neighbour kids when I was little. We played cowboys. I was Zorro. That's finished, though, me and Zorro. He's a good guy and he always wins. I want to be a bad guy and win. Ought to find another kid for the good guy so we could fight. The time would go quicker.

To think I once imagined Pa was a big strong man! All he can do is bellyache about the government and men who don't mean a thing to me. If he doesn't like what they're doing he should go and tell them, and push their faces in. He's yellow. To think I once counted on him! He's even scared of Ma. When she says, " 'Phonse, that'll do," it's funny and sad to see him put his head down and shut up and go sit in the rocker. Great example for the kids.

There's mud all over. Sand and melting ice. Makes kind of a soup. I get kicks out of stamping in it and splashing people. They get mad and scream like murder. Don't think it's funny at all. If they did it to me, I'd laugh. A little mud won't kill anyone.

It's good when winter goes. You feel you won't freeze to death any more. You open like a flower, and start to breathe, and look at the sky, and you're glad to feel the wind, even if it's bringing bad weather. You can stop long enough to crack a joke or hum a little tune you've got jigging round in your head. Us kids can go out in the evening. Aren't made to do homework any more. There's a smell of rot everywhere, and the sparrows tumble about from window to window and go pecking around the corners of yards.

The girls skip rope . . . one, two, three. . . . "Good enough to eat," says Pa, sucking on his pipe. I make fun of them because they're scared to go to the market with me.

"I'm going for a walk, Ma."

"Yes, Sonny, but don't be late."

"I'll come back when it gets dark."

In April it gets dark pretty soon. You don't expect it and all of a sudden it's there, like a curtain between the sky and the street. Big purple, red and blue patches crowd each other in the sky. It glows dark when the sun comes through. Like a dump full of colours.

Since I've been snitching alone I've got no friends any more. They do it in gangs and they're jealous. Hum-m-m. . . . Still open at Valiquette's. That's right. Friday's nine o'clock closing. Ought to try it in a big store like that.

That's how it happened.

I went in and had a good look round. Sporting goods on the second floor. A beautiful little hatchet just like I'd always wanted. A wheezing, paunchy salesman with beetle eyebrows was watching me. In a flash I grabbed the hatchet and took off. Ran like mad. Bumped a woman, then a little girl. Then whack! . . . bang into the edge of a door. I threw myself this way and that, from one side of the store to the other, holding my nose and my bleeding mouth. They cornered me, the bastards, caught me between two doors. I was mad. My face was on fire and my rear too. When the police came there were salesmen pinning my arms down and insulting me. I didn't cry, I swear it, not a goddam tear. But I did spit blood all over a cop.!

The rest just happened. The preaching, the juvenile court bit, my mother blubbering to her "gracious lordship" and my father cursing as he rolled his Exports. I kept my mouth shut, except I swore I'd be at it again once I was out. The grownups didn't go for that, and they kept me a good long time in the reformatory. It was like school twenty-four hours a day. I'll tell you about that later. . . .

One day they let me go. . . . But Bonsecours Market wasn't there any more. It had gone, as though it had only been another dream. Then I did cry for sure. Not very long, 'cause I got tired of it. Pa seemed pretty glum. Ma'd just had an operation, but they didn't tell me what for. I still had my lane, but there was nobody there except me, all alone. So I started telling stories, like this one. . . .

Jacques Renaud

The Coat-Rack

Jacques Renaud (b. 1943) is the most experimental of the *joual* group. His novel *Le Cassé* (1964), translated in an abridged version by Gerald Robitaille as *Flat Broke and Beat,* was as liberating for young writers in the late 'sixties as Bessette's *Le Libraire* was in the late 'fifties. Unfortunately he has not published much since.

In this short story one can ascertain the alienation and bitterness which characterize much young separatist writing to-day. But there is also a wry humour and a Ducharme-like inventiveness with language that makes it one of the most amusing and unusual pieces in this collection.

Ronald Bates is Professor of English at the University of Western Ontario. He has published three books of poetry and a study of Northrop Frye. He has already translated poems from Finnish and Swedish but this is his first prose translation from the French-Canadian.

The Coat-Rack

Bent
above
the
glistening side-
walk of St. Matthieu
Street, his face was diluted
by cold undulations that crawled—meandered as the
Scotch crawled limpid white, dilating his retinas—crawled the length
of his throat, little explosions in the machine for making deliriums
and dizziness, some place between the heart and the stomach.

The rain annoyed him, chilled his neck, his coat grew heavy with
water, he bent his head, his shoulders, above the moving pavement
of St. Matthieu Street, slipping and sliding, bent over the remains of
his twelve ounces of Black and White, his twelve-ouncer, let slip his
twelve-ouncer, moment of inattention popped out between the
pocket of his overcoat and his drunken hand.

The rain ran off the end of his nose, he submitted to the elements,
the wind bent the branches of the trees towards the west of Montreal, he bowed, he bowed towards the jagged debris of his twelve-
ouncer bust in the same cardinal direction as the branches of the
trees, I should have listened to the weather report weatheroroscope
weatheraugury, available to all, just turn a button and the secrets of
the sky are delivered to you, its inventory made, its secrets, probable
and verifiable, delivered completely fresh to you.

I should have listened to the weatheraugury, couldn't foresee that
I'd be drunk as a skunk all alone, that it would rain, that my twelve-
ouncer would sink into the sidewalk moving in dancing trances
down St. Matthieu Street, my Black and White black thoughts in a
white glare for this French-Canadian translator.

My gargle-scraper, my nipple, my reinvagination. Back bowed,
stagger, lose footing, glass breaking crunching under my foot going
to smash up my very own little mickey. . . .

"Got to get those loose tiles fixed. . . . Almost fell again. . . ."

"Call Fred. . . ."

Yes, I'm going to call little Fred. Personnel director for an English-Canadian translation agency. Scottish type. If he were a French Canadian he'd be assistant sweeper in the furnace room, would little Fred. With his scope, his intelligence, he'd be a sweeper, little Fred would.

Yes, I'll call him. At once. Not brilliant, with his square little head. Inspires a racist lyricism in me. But of the best, of the chemical English for ridiculosary consumption. Just the same, going to talk to him. Me, I'm going to tell him that those damned tiles, almost smash my face stumbling over them every time I come into my office like a gust of wind—*en coup de vent* just like that, thas what I'm going to tell him, like *un vent féroce* north wind that bows me down the rain freeze his bones stare at each other stare at the dizziness some place between the heart and the stomach don't close the eyes or it's falling into the glaucous and glacial depths of the sidewalk on St. Matthieu Street—it's like that every time I come in likezeweend every time wind of gust a like office my into come I, I shove my foot under the upper lip of one of those curled up tiles almost smash my face in—doan chiou understand that when *ça m'arrive* I look like a minus an' it humiliates me, see?

"That's ridicoulousse. . . ."

Thas what little Fred said, with an indignant look. He's going to get them fixed and damned quick. That's for sure. Tiles that curl up on the floor of an agency of twelve-ounce calibre, twice, sometimes three times a week. . . .

In his office with its all-white walls this translator has stuck up two reproductions. Oddbirds in a tree by Kieko Minami and Bull Ring *par* Pablo Picasso. Minami, some zmall black birds on a turquoise background picking at some red cherries in a tree with a trunk the shape of a fish tail zmall black birds on a turquoise background twit-twit-twit terou douzou gouzou gonna get them yet those anglos have puerile attitudes you'd like to make them gouzee gouzee one day they'll give out with their zmall black fowl trills in the middle of the noise of typewriters and the inhibited fantasms of the stenos and the boss in the middle of all that chattering from one office to another, the laughing, the bursts of voices, end up by tossing them off, pitching them out burping them up those stomach burning trills gourgou yum yum zmall birds never even had the idea they might yank themselves out of the reproduction—even though they're two, two heads better than one, bird brains, degenerate paper poultry with no taste for freedom, no fools they, but not bright either, stuck there in their esthetics, in Minami's colour and will, but no window in my office, the walls are white all white, it's the biggest office on the floor situated in *l'immeuble* CANADA CEMENT building *place* PHILLIPS square, all white, I also have a desk, three chairs, one swivel, a coat-rack, brown, I put in the middle of the office. The coat-rack that is.

The cleaning man decided that it wasn't orthodox, that a coat-rack should be placed in a corner and that its place is not in the middle of the office. That must have disturbed him, a coat-rack in the middle of an office.

We played hide-and-seek for two weeks, the cleaning man and I. When I arrived in the morning I would find the coat-rack in the corner. I would replace it in the middle of the office, I would hang my coat on it. The next morning I would find it in a corner, like a dead tree in disgrace.

So I'd put it in the middle of the office again. It was more like nature that way. A tree in the middle of a field of turnips. With the two zmall birds by Minami, that made a not too dismal still life. Nothing missing but the fountain.

In the middle of the office my coat-rack signified something. I say *my* coat-rack because by shifting an object, by imparting a movement to it which it obeys, to which it conforms, one possesses that object, doesn't one, I have the impression of being very much in possession of what I shift, transform, modify. It was *my* coat-rack after I had transformed it into a tree in the middle of a field of turnips, after I had, in its name, entered into cunning and subversive battle with the cleaning man (orthodoxy) for the delimitation of frontiers, for the determination of the final place which would be that of (*this* or *my*) coat-rack, the prize, the Alcazar, the fort at Long-Sault.

That coat-rack had class, my coat-rack did. One would have said a gallows, when I looked at it attentively. My eventual execution stake. For that matter the agency employees had begun to look at me queerly, at first an amused mimicry on their faces, then annoyed looks, and some hostile expressions, distinctly hostile. What at the start was only an amusing game—for them—quickly became with the passing minutes, hours, days, quickly became a questioning of the established order in the office, an insupportable questioning: a disquieting lack of orthodoxy on my part. . . .

Some days I took myself for Him. I thought of myself as at the Gesu theatre during the presentation of the play of Saint-Denys. I became the only and unique hero of the play, the coat-rack in the middle of the stage to which I would be tied, or would transfix myself, entangled in thousands of miles of typewriter ribbon, black and red, choked, employed, salaried.

I gave in.

One morning, I went into my office. The coat-rack remained in the corner. The janitor had won the victory. It was no longer *my* coat-rack. It was the-coat-rack-in-the-corner-of-the-office, not even *the* coat-rack, a stupid word, I denied it, I was ashamed of it, I was dispossessed.

It is no longer dangerous, annoying, no one is going to hang himself on it. My coat, yes: all day long. But a coat isn't susceptible to polemic. With the coat on it, the coat-rack now made me think of a scarecrow. Five o'clock. I stretch out my arm. I take a coat... in my fingertips. . . .

A hand crashes down on my shoulder. Fear. Nerves. I turn around.

"For Chrissake! Quit pullin' on the straw of the scarecrow. You're gonna make the crows come back."

Claude Jasmin

Pygmalion
Rosaire

In his forty-three years Claude Jasmin has practised
nearly every *métier* in the field of letters—essayist, journalist, dramatist, biographer, scenarist, critic, novelist and
short story writer. He is best known in English Canada for his novel *Ethel and the Terrorist* (1964), translated
by David Walker. His most unjustly neglected novel is
the much less sensational *Pleure pas, Germaine* (1965), a
piece of low-key social realism that is disconcerting in its
naturalness and humanity.

The two stories included here come from *Les Coeurs
empaillés* (1967), Jasmin's only collection of short stories.
They illustrate the directness of his approach and the
brash, aggressive style that characterizes much of his
writing. Which is not to say that they are short on
tenderness—it just situates him as one of Quebec's angry
young men.

Marc Plourde is a poet. He has published two volumes:
Touchings, with Fiddlehead, and *The White Magnet*, with
D and C Press. He is currently working on a volume of
short stories to be called *The Flies in the Glass*, and a
translation of Juan Garcia's *The Alchemy of the Body*.

Pygmalion

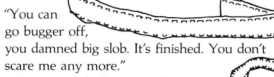

"You can
go bugger off,
you damned big slob. It's finished. You don't
scare me any more."

Potvin, no fool, was sniffing at
her. He wheeled round her like a
maddened dog. He'd like to have
beaten her. He was no fool. He knew very well that she had changed.
So, it was finished, eh? Finished? He had made a woman of her. A
true woman. Now she was acting independent. But she would be
nothing, less than nothing, if he, Ferdinand Potvin, hadn't been there
when she had fallen.

"Listen Huguette. . . ."

"No more 'Listen Huguette'. Let me be."

She gets up from her seat, walks toward a corner of the hall. He
still follows her.

"I feel like tearing your eyes out. You're disgusting. I did everything for you. I wasted my time. I wasted my life. You know that?
I could've had work in New York. You know that, Huguette?"

At that, she turns red. Like a tomato. She turns round and comes
right up to him. She sticks a finger in his ribs:

"You're not going to put on that old record? You're not going to
start that again? That's dead and gone, your New York story. I
screamed at you a hundred times, a thousand times, to go work for
your damned idiot magazines. All you had to do was go!"

He stands stupefied. He looks at her, eyes bulging.

"Huguette! But—but you were bawling your head off. You were
bawling. Try to remember. It was Christmas Eve. We were at your
brother-in-law's farm. Your eyes were filled with tears."

"That's not the same. During the holidays it doesn't count. I'm a
bawl-baby. It doesn't count. Now get out, bug off. The sooner you
leave, the better it'll be for everyone. Can't you understand that?"

Ferdinand is scraping the floor with his foot. He looks around him. Dozens of couples are bouncing and shaking their bodies hysterically. He's horrified by that. Huguette gets herself picked up by a tall guy with long red hair to his shoulders. She starts swinging with everyone else to the rhythm of the drummer and twelve electric guitars. You can't hear yourself think. She laughs.

She is laughing, thinks Ferdinand. She is laughing. So she can laugh, at least. She never laughed. It's true, he can go now. He can very well disappear. She doesn't need him any more. It's true. What use is he to her now? Girls like to change teachers. One for this, one for that. Girls are fickle by nature.

Still, he had thought, for life. She had fallen so low. So low? Maybe not so low after all. He had built up illusions for himself. It happens often enough, it's not the end of the world, it's a very ordinary event: a child that first sees the light of day in a small private hospital on St. Denis street. Every day they're born, these little love-bastards. Oh yes, he had been sentimental. He had coaxed her. Advised her. Had been a father, a real father to her. She was twenty. He was ten years older. Easy to play father, consoler. The true-blue friend, the advisor, the slicky, the smart one, the wise guy. Very easy. Deep down, Ferdinand, the role suited you nicely. The noble knight! As if you had got nothing out of the situation.

"I'm a bloody hypocrite. I'm a big softy."

Poor Ferdinand. Good old Ferdie. Photographer from nine to five for national television. A good boy. A well-brought-up little boy from Gaspé Street. Good manners. Good marks on his school report cards. Conduct: always Very Good. Often Excellent. A respectable boy. A little timid. Considerate. Polite to fellow parishioners. Prone to illness: his lungs. The timid person's sickness: weak lungs. Prolonged internment. A stay in the Laurentians. Studies postponed. This trade: photography. And one night, a little girl crying. He picks her up the way you pick up a broken flower. He dreams. Every student in the world wants to save whores. Ferdinand picks her up out of the traditional gutter. He washes her, powders her, makes her up, makes her sit on stools, makes her smile, spins her around, makes her bite a flower, makes her pose, makes her laugh. He saves her, I tell you, he saves her. Then he thinks: She owes me her life!

But Huguette, she's not that kind. She's tired of posing, smiling, lifting her mane of hair, showing her teeth, biting flowers, perching on black and white stools, on rolls of gold paper, for the magazines. *169 + Pygmalion*

She's still young, she wants to talk, she wants to laugh and sing. She wants to be heard. She's not an image. She's not a ball of clay in Pygmalion's hands. She's met people. Everywhere it's the age of talk. And she's still dumb. Photography? It nauseates her. She wants to get into theatre. She wants to do movies, television. She wants to talk at the top of her voice.

Ferdinand leaves. Dance halls are always the same, smoke and noise. Yes, it's finished. What ingratitude. He's so surprised. Then she didn't owe him her life after all? He'd been dreaming. He walks out into the night. He crosses the field behind the hall, a shortcut to get home faster. He no longer has any family. He broke off with his folks. Such a horror, this pregnant girl! He's lost everything, he thinks. That's what comes of staking everything on one hope. The poor dear. The poor kid. So he no longer even has his mummy, or his daddy, who is very angry. The good parents had hoped for so much from their well-brought-up big boy who greeted all the parishioners every Sunday on Gaspé Street.

Ferdinand hurries on, for he hears the sound of weeping in the night, moaning. He closes his eyes a bit. He no longer wants to see these demons, these girls, broken by horrible sins, begging him. The days of his sainthood are well past. Let them get along without me from now on, he thinks. All of them, ingrates! He walks toward his family's house. Toward mummy who will forgive the prodigal son. Toward the home of all the sweet things he should never have left. But this episode with Huguette, it was such a acandal in the family! He returns to the fold. Big Ferdinand. The big drip.

And mummy cries. She forgives him. It's good to find that which was lost. Daddy coughs, clears his throat and is restless. He's going to make coffee—like a good grog-of-pardon—and he thinks, Well, it's just a few more dishes to wash, that's all. For he's a good daddy, a real brick; they don't make them like that any more. Ferdinand smiles, cries, snivels. Ah, how sweet is the sweetness of home, found again after months and months of absence.

"So console yourself," says mummy-with-red-eyes. "You have a good job, security. Why make trouble for yourself? Why get mixed up with a woman? I am here, always, my little dear."

And mummy coos on the shoulder of her good, big, fat boy. The kitchen on Gaspé Street is oozing tenderness. We'll see Ferdinand again on Sunday, at the end of high mass. "Like in the good old days," sigh daddy and mummy. And he'll give nice big "how-do-you-do's" to all the parishioners.

Ferdinand, who is nobody's fool, knows very well that all this, this offensive kindness, is as phony as shit, but what do you expect? He tells himself that he'll become completely "faggy". It will be Huguette's fault. Tomorrow morning he'll go see Ivon; he'll wheel him around in his wheelchair. Like before. And then, to pass the evening, he'll go to big Saint-Onge's physical culture studio. They'll feel each other's biceps and all the rest, like before. Ah, too bad, too bad. It's Huguette's fault if all that starts over again.

But he hit a snag. Big Saint-Onge was no longer there. He had to sublet his studio and was gone, far away, no one knew where. A funny story. It was the curate-in-charge-of-sports who had told him all that. "He had been imprudent," he explained to him, with eager eyes. And then, the good curate-in-charge-of-sports had showed him all the new arrangements. Especially the Turkish bath. They laughed a lot. Ferdinand didn't know much about how it worked. And the curate, in BVDs, red with sweat and excitement, helped him out.

Next morning Ferdinand bravely returned to work. In his small office he found a note: *Urgent. See the producer, Saint-Amand.* He walked up to Saint-Amand's office. Saint-Amand, the silly, detestable playboy of the variety shows, said to him: "Later this morning I'm sending a young thing in to you. I need a good dozen photos of this adorable starlet. I'm presenting her as hostess on The Hen That Lays the Golden Turds. Her name is Huguette Plamondon. You'll be in your office?"

And Ferdinand walked out, red as a cock. Huguette?

He walked back up to Saint-Amand's office fifteen minutes later with fourteen dozen photographs of pretty Huguette. And he left again in silence. It was as if he had come to pass on his love letters to the next-in-line.

Rosaire

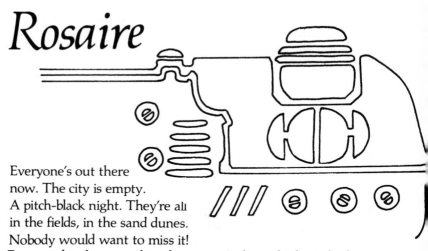

Everyone's out there now. The city is empty. A pitch-black night. They're all in the fields, in the sand dunes. Nobody would want to miss it! Every night, the same thing happens. At first, a high-pitched sound, like a sharp whistling. And then, flashes in the sky. Finally, you can make out a sort of great brown mass. It seems immense. The day before yesterday, it hid the moon, it was so huge. You'd think— this is an impression—that you could touch it if you climbed a high ladder. This is the sixth night this has recurred. The second night was a shock, a surprise. It happened the same hour as the night before. The same noises, the same flashes. On the third night, there was already a crowd. When the police and radio station helicopters went up to take a closer look, the great mass suddenly melted, erased itself in an instant among "Oh's" of disappointment. Just like that, like a mirage of water on a summer road. So the fourth day they arranged things differently. Some people from Oka got together and formed "The Committee for the Freedom of the Thing". They asked the radio stations to ground the helicopters; they begged the Provincial Police to do the same. And it was strange, strange to see this crowd gathered on the fifth night, mute and observant, to listen to the whistling sound, to watch the luminous blinks, to observe this great dome that was landing which, you would think, was settling itself on four invisible corners, always over the same area, in the sand dunes behind Calumet Point. It was hideous. It was brown, ochre-yellow, and it looked like some kind of war machine, because of its texture: a sort of shell covered with pimples. Was it bolts? Screws? "It was an animal's hide!" For several wags talked about a mysterious beast that had got lost in the universe and been attracted to this vicinity either, according to some, by the nearby lake, or, according to others, by the radio towers. They also said that some boys on an expedition in the Oka mountains, had discovered strange craters. "The animal takes great mouthfuls of trees!"

This night, the sixth night then, the crowd was immense. They had come from everywhere: from Montréal, of course, but also from farther off, from Three Rivers, from Hull, and there was even a considerable number of licence plates from Ontario and the States. Everyone, noses in the air, was looking at the phenomenon. The cover had settled, it seemed, and the people were happy about that. In the middle of the crowd, a great empty space had been left open. You never know. Some part of the mechanism, or a message, or a memento of some kind might fall out of it. Hearts were beating fast. The wildest rumours were circulating. That afternoon some nut had written on the ground the word *Welcome* in four languages, by emptying bags of lime as on a baseball field.

It seemed that time had stopped, had frozen clean in its tracks. People frequently consulted their watches. Because nothing was happening. Nothing more than this opaque block, this immense dome that lay flat in the sky, over the heads lifted towards it. The first nights, motorists had played with their car horns as if to salute the newcomers from the cosmos. They also played with the headlights, blinking them on and off, on and off, as if to answer the flashes that always preceded the machine's arrival. There was a sense of contemplation, a mixture of apprehension and anticipation of something better or something worse. So what was going to happen?

Yesterday, on the fifth night, the day after the helicopters' lamentable intrusion, the machine, the wall, the thing, the shell covered with bolts, disappeared at about midnight, and in the same sequence: disappearance of the plate in the night air, then blinking flashes and, lastly, the shrill whistles. And as always, after all that, there was a sort of heaviness in the air, puffs of soft, warm wind. The silence was becoming heavy, alarming even. From minute to minute and then hour to hour, everyone hoped to see something happen. We are always so eager for the unexpected. It wasn't enough any more always to see this big, dull-coloured dome comfortably and almost indecently installed in the sky over Two Mountains County. People wanted more. They hoped hard that the amazing machine would not disappear as it had done the day before, just at midnight. That was too stupid! This time, something else would happen. Something new.

Midnight came and, far from its disappearing, a hundred, a thousand sockets began to revolve on the dome's surface. A hundred, a thousand ladders descended, unrolling themselves slowly, just like at the circus. A thousand hands reached up, willing to help.

There was a rumble of murmurs. Children started nervously clapping. Adults were shaken by sharp, uncontrollable laughter. No one dared to advance into the great circle where the four *Welcomes* were written.

Nothing moved any more. Nothing, neither being nor machine, came out or appeared on one of these white cord ladders, or near the dome's revolving socket-doors.

And no one dared make a move. Big Rosaire, the village idiot, shouted, shaking her long mane of white hair: "I'm going, I'm going to climb up, I am." But the Chief of Police shouted into his loudspeaker, "Nobody move." And, in a lower voice, as if fearing ridicule, "Maybe they've set a trap, they . . . them . . . the machine." He coughed, ill at ease, embarrassed. Long minutes that seemed hours passed.

People were sitting down in the sand. They handed around innumerable pairs of binoculars. The most unbelievable stories were circulating: tiny beings were afraid to come down; armies of bloodthirsty robots were going to pour out!

Suddenly someone shouted, "It's eight o'clock! It's eight o'clock!" You could see thousands of heads bend down. The watches *did* all actually say eight o'clock. Time had passed, in spite of everything. While everyone was waiting. It was eight o'clock in the morning. And it was still like night. The immense dome therefore covered a space much greater than anyone had believed. It was unbelievable. The Chief of Police ran to his car radio. It was true. At St. Eustache it was night, at Ste. Thérèse too, and on the other side of the lake, at Como, at Vaudreuil, and north, at St. Jérôme too. The radio announcers were pouring out the news bulletins. Yes, it was night everywhere. Dawn had not come. From every direction you could see, more or less clearly, depending on the region, this dome, this monstrous, ugly shell. They found it ugly now, frightening. You could read panic in all their faces. It was the last judgment. The country would be wiped out. It was the Russians, the Chinese. This was the end. The end of the world?

From everywhere news bulletins came in by radio. It was also night at Québec, at Rimouski, in the Gaspé, in Vermont, and over the Mississippi. It was dreadful. Dawn no longer came up over the Gulf of Mexico, nor the Atlantic, nor over the Pacific either. It was disgusting. It was the end of the world, really, the end of the world!

Some old people started singing hymns and reciting prayers. Cars pulled out with a lot of ruckus and squealing tires. People were crying and shouting. Many were leaving. It was the most terrible deception. They no longer looked up at that lousy roof of yellowish shit. They looked at each other, they held hands. They bawled. The car radios threw gloom into everyone's soul. It was the same night everywhere. The same goddam brown shell! The same infernal roof. There was nothing to do but to go back to your home, to your room, to lie down on your bed and prepare to die. Everyone was shoving each other, everyone going home. So this was the end of the world, the end of time? It was too stupid. God really lacked imagination! Really. It was sordid. And you couldn't expect anything worse. For what is worse than losing heaven's light, the warm light of day? You couldn't imagine. A night soon passed, and day always came back. . . .

The site was empty now. The radio and its horrible "Darkness everywhere" news bulletins had made everyone forget the dome and its stupid ladders.

Rosaire had stayed behind. She took out her harmonica and started to play a tune from the old days. She shook it and wiped the harmonica on her sleeve. She approached the centre of the field. Innocently, she put out a hand to touch one of the cord ladders. And all the ladders quickly wound themselves back up. The small doors in the sockets closed again. And the huge shell started melting away. This time, there were no flashes, no whistling. Nothing but the sun that suddenly lit up the ground and the sand hills, right here. Everywhere, people exulted. You could hear them laughing and singing from city to city, by God!

Rosaire took out her marmonica again and lifted her head to the sun, grinning. This time she played the very best she could.

ACKNOWLEDGEMENTS

Nouvelles Editions de l'Arc for: "The Bus Driver", "The Buyer",
and "The Wall" by Gilles Vigneault.

Marie-Clair, Blais and Nouvelles Editions de l'Arc for "The New
Schoolmistress" from *Le Testament de Jean le Maigre* by Marie-Claire
Blais.

Editions Hurtubise for: "Animal Husbandry" and "Martine Continued"
by Jacques Ferron; "Sugar Heart" and "Be Fruitful and Multiply"
by Madeline Ferron.

Jacques Renaud for "The Coat-Rack".

Gérard Bessette for "The Mustard Plaster".

Partis Pris for: "The Thief of Bonsecours Market" by André Major;
"Pygmalion" and "Rosaire" by Claude Jasmin.

Le Cercle du Livre de France for: "Jos-la-Fiole" by Roger Fournier;
"The 48 Hour Pass" by Jean-Jules Richard; "Back on April Eleven"
by Hubert Aquin; "Follow Me", and "Springtime" by Claire Martin.

Editions Gallimard for "The Wedding Gown" from *Le Nez qui Voque*
by Réjean Ducharme.

Les Editions du Jour for: "The Bird", "The Ink", and "Creation" by
Roch Carrier; "The Shipwreck" by François Hertel; "The Great
Disappearing Act" by Jean Tetreau; "The Hanged Man", "Mister
Blank", "The Thimble" by Michel Tremblay; "Akua Nuten" by Yves
Theriault.